RECOVERY EQUATION

Logotherapy, Psychodrama & Choice Awareness Training
for Substance Use/Addictions Treatment

PAVEL GEORGIEVICH SOMOV, PH.D

TRAIN OF THOUGHT PRESS

Recovery Equation: Logotherapy, Psychodrama & Choice Awareness
Training for Substance Use/Addictions Treatment

Copyright © 2008 by Pavel G. Somov, Ph.D./Train of Thought Press

ISBN 978-0-557-02215-1

Table of Contents

Change Equation: Introduction

Introduction to the Change Equation Model

The Change Equation Model is a technical synthesis of several schools of clinical and philosophical thought, and is predicated on a unifying algorithm of change referred to henceforth as the Change Equation. The Change Equation Model is specifically intended for the treatment of the compulsive/addictive spectrum of psychological presentations. The present volume, however, details the application of this approach to the problem of substance use.

The Recovery Equation Method

The Recovery Equation, or the Motivational Enhancement, Choice Awareness, and Use Prevention Therapy (ME/CA/UP), is a secular application of the Change Equation Model to the problem of substance abuse. The Recovery Equation is specifically designed to augment the treatment of substance abuse in the context of an intensive inpatient or intensive outpatient (daily partial hospitalization) drug and alcohol treatment program.

Clinical and Philosophical Context

In its conceptual orientation and its technical eclecticism, the Change Equation Model, and its substance use specific application, the Recovery Equation, draw from the following schools of clinical thought, theoretical and research domains (in alphabetical order):

- Acceptance and Commitment Therapy (Hayes et al., 1999)

- Cognitive Behavioral Relapse Prevention Therapy (Marlatt & Gordon, 1985)

- Cognitive Dissonance Theory (Festinger, 1957)

- Crystallization of Discontent (Baumeister, 1996)

- Exposure/Response Prevention Therapy (Drummond et al., 1995)

- Feedback-loop Theory of Self-Regulation (Baumeister, 1994)

- The Philosophy of Gurdjieff (Speeth, 1989; Ouspensky, 1949)

- Inoculation Hypothesis (McGuire, 1964) and Stress Inoculation Training (Meichenbaum, 1993)

- Logotherapy (Frankl, 1969)

- Motivational Interviewing Therapy (Miller & Rollnick, 1991; Saunders et al., 1991)

- Relational Frame Theory (Hayes, 1987)

- Self-Change Research (Klingemann et al, 2001)

- Self-Efficacy Theory (Bandura, 1982)

The Change Equation as a Unifying Theory

The business of clinical psychology – regardless of the actual treatment goals – is that of facilitating a client's change, from one state to another. A number of years ago, while trying to conceive a personal framework for a change process, I stumbled upon Frankl's quotation of Nietzsche's "he who knows a 'why' for living, will surmount almost any 'how'" (Lonergan, 1999; p. 107).

If transcribed as a change process, Nietzsche's thought could be represented as a change equation as follows:

Change = the Why

Or,

Change = Reason to Change

In pondering this change recipe, I appreciated Frankl's forceful endorsement of strategic, personally-relevant meaning as the driving motivation behind a change from the state of meaningless suffering and despair to the state of existential resilience.

A further review of his work, however, convinced me that while motivation is critical to the change process, motivation, in itself, is only predictive of an attempt at change but is not a guarantor of change. Aside from motivation, a specific change process requires a specific set of skills. Consequently, the Change Equation needed a revision: the Why had to be complemented with the How.

Change = the Why + the How

Or,

Change = Reason to Change + Method to Change

After toying with the Change Equation above, I realized a final missing link: in order for one to change, one has to be free. Freedom, while fundamental and inalienable, is, nevertheless, a perceptual variable, not a constant, in any equation of change. And indeed, while we at any given moment have at least two or more options (or degrees of freedom), we often feel that we have no choice.

In pondering the difference between actual and perceived freedom, I realized that there are two barriers to one's phenomenological sense of freedom. They are: 1) cognitive-affective-behavioral automaticity, and 2) freedom-restricting belief structures.

Freedom manifests itself through awareness of choice. The more choices we have, the more degrees of freedom we have. With this in mind, both issues (the automaticity and the freedom-restricting belief structure) are synonymous with lack of choice awareness. Consequently, the change algorithm had to be complimented with the notion of Choice Awareness or its semantic counterpart, the Freedom to Change.

Change = the Awareness of Choice + the Why + the How

Or,

Change = Freedom to Change + Reason to Change + Method to Change

With this equation in mind, it could be then summarized that the change is predicated on the three change variables: Reason to Change (the Why, or the Motivation), the Freedom to Change (as manifested by Awareness of Choice), and Method to Change (the How, a task-specific skill-set, or Skill-Power).

Interplay of the 3 Change Variables

All three Change Variables have to be in place in order to attain an enduring life-style change. As such, each of the three variables is equi-important but equi-insufficient, in itself. Metaphorically, change can be likened to a journey by car. Reason to Change corresponds to the motivational fuel/gas in the tank. Freedom to Change corresponds to the steering wheel that navigates various decisional forks on the road to a destination. Method to Change represents the wheels and other mechanical infrastructure of the car that translates the motivational energy and the direction guidance of choice into the actual movement of the vehicle towards a change destination.

The Recovery Equation Method

As noted above, the Recovery Equation method is a specific application of the Change Equation Model. The Recovery Equation may be clinically expressed as follows:

Recovery = Choice Awareness Training + Motivational Enhancement + Use Prevention Training

With these clinically-stated change components in mind, the specific goals of the Recovery Equation Method, in application to the problem of substance use, are as follows:

a)   to assist the substance-use client in developing intrinsic motivation for change that can withstand any change in circumstance;

b)   to assist the client in developing strategic and tactical awareness of choice;

c)   to assist the client in developing use prevention skills that include craving control; slip prevention, lapse prevention, relapse prevention, and relapse termination plans; emotional self-regulation skills and a knowledge-base on the socially-sanctioned, psychologically, physically, financially and legally safer natural highs; and interpersonal skills.

As a clinical curriculum, the Recovery Equation consists of the following list of psycho-educational, process, and self-help groups, and individual therapy modalities:

Reason to Change Modalities:

- Search-for-Why Self-Help Circle
- Meaning of Life Group
- Drugs, Health & Self Concept Group
- Your Loss – Their Gain Group

- Motivation Check Group

- Epiphany Type Motivational Enhancement

Freedom to Change Modalities:

- Choice Awareness Training Group

- Choice Awareness Practice Group

- Choice Awareness Check Group

Method to Change Modalities:

- Relaxation Training Group

- Craving Control Training Group

- Craving Control Practice Group

- Natural Highs Group

- Duality-Based Emotional Self-Regulation Group

- Introduction to Use Prevention Group

- Lapse/Relapse Prevention Practice Group

- Interpersonal Process Group

- Individual Psychotherapy (Supportive and/or Axis I/II and/or Behavioral Medicine)

- Skill-power Check Group

The 5 Principles of the Change Equation Method

In designing and practicing the Change Equation method, I have guided myself with a set of dialectic treatment principles that I have come to view as integral to a successful clinical execution of the Change Equation method.

These five dialectic principles are as follows:

Principle 1: Humanize/Automatize

Principle 2: Validate/Sublimate

Principle 3: Motivate/Inoculate

Principle 4: Catastrophize/Decatastrophize

Principle 5: De-Automatize/Re-Automatize

The following is an explanation of each principle, its rationale, and its role in delivering the Change Equation method in clinical practice.

Humanize/Automatize

This principle conveys a dialectic clinical stance that, on one hand, involves Humanization of the Problem, and, on the other hand, involves Automatization of the Solution to the Problem.

Humanize

There are no non-human problems. Any problem, be it abuse of a substance, of a food, or of a child, is a human creation. While I might earn the Obvious Statement of the Day Award for this pronouncement, this cliché holds an important curative power.

The clinical school of Logotherapy understands this quite well. Substance use, among other forms of abuse, is seen in a highly existential, and, therefore, humanistic context. In particular, substance use may be conceptualized as defining the meaning of life in terms of pleasure or experiential self-exploration. Alternatively, substance use may be existentially conceptualized as an escape from meaninglessness of life. Either way, Logotherapists appreciate that substance use is a very human issue, and do not rush to pathologize it.

Buddhism also understands the humanity of substance use. Addiction, from the Buddhist standpoint, is a road more traveled. In my book "Egg Drop Soup for the Mind" I propose that "Addiction is inverted Buddhism. The latter is death-less-ness through mind-ful-ness. The former is life-less-ness through mind-less-ness" (Somov, 2003).

Both Addiction (A) and Buddhism (B) kill the existential angst, which may be further subdivided into fear of life (as in intolerance of distress, anxiety, tension, emotional lows) and into fear of death (fear of non-existence, loneliness, emptiness). Buddhism kills the fear of death by keeping the mind full of life that is omnipresent in any given moment. By focusing the mind on the moment to the point of the loss of distinction between self and other, subject and object, Buddhism accomplishes a sense of oneness, a powerful antidote to feelings of emptiness or loneliness or invalidation, which are but different manifestations of fear of death and nonexistence.

Addiction, on the other hand, kills the fear of life by keeping the mind numb, anesthetized, mind-less. Addiction literally obliterates one's sense of self: when under the influence you cease to exist as the psychological entity that you are. Your mind, your consciousness, for the duration of the drug's half-life, is altered. An altered mind-state is a changed mind-state. The original mind-state that you are is no longer, and a new mind-state, governed by simpler limbic algorithms, replaces you at the steering wheel of your body. Consequently, both the "mindless-ness" of Addiction (A) and the "mind-ful-ness" of Buddhism (B) are but different means to a state of Contentedness (C).

The Change Equation method recognizes addiction as a legitimate coping choice. While not to be mistaken as an endorsement, such a position humanizes clients' life-long struggle for emotional self-regulation in the pursuit of Contentedness (C).

The Change Equation method facilitators assist clients in an open examination of the relative pros and cons of Life with Presence of Mind (Mind-ful-ness) and Life with Absence of Mind (Mind-less-ness). By acknowledging that both are legitimate understandable choices, the Change Equation humanizes the choice to use drugs and/or alcohol. In fact, the Change Equation method congratulates the client for any choice he or she makes, and, in the event that the client chooses a Path of Absence (through substance use), facilitators acknowledge that a choice to make no choices is, indeed, the client's prerogative.

Automatize

While the humanistic, existential, and phenomenological philosophies Humanize the Problem (in this case, of substance use), they fall short of Automatizing the Solution to the Problem. Humans are automatons. Automatization, therefore, is a very human mode of functioning. In fact, automatization is one of the most powerful problem-solving tools that the human mind has devised.

Behaviorists understand this quite well. Whereas Victor Frankl and Carl Rogers may help you humanize the problem that you have, Pavlov, Skinner, and Watson know something about automatizing the solution to the problem.

Substance use does not become abuse until it becomes automatized. Problematic drinking or drugging are phenomenologically-human solutions that, by virtue of conditioning on bio-psycho-environmental cues, have become problems in themselves. While the traditional substance use treatment approaches pull off a fairly decent job with humanizing the problem, they fail in automatizing the solution. Conditioned problems, to be solved, require de-conditioning, re-conditioning, and over-conditioning of the solutions.

With this in mind, the Change Equation both humanizes the problem and automatizes the solutions through massed practice of several key skills. Therefore, using the designation of the often orthogonally positioned clinical camps, the Change Equation assumes, among other clinical postures, a rather infrequent EP/CB stance (existential-phenomenological/cognitive-behavioral) which can be otherwise captured as the Principle of Humanize/Automatize.

Validate/Sublimate

This principle conveys a dialectic clinical stance that, on one hand, psycho-dynamically validates one's personality liabilities, and, on the other hand, psycho-analytically sublimates these liabilities into socially-acceptable assets.

Validate

Psychological flukes do not exist. You are everything you have ever been. Therefore, you are psychologically pre-determined. No, not the choice you make, but how you make these choices. If you are a narcissist, an antisocial, an avoidant, an obsessive-compulsive, a histrionic, that's ok. You did not choose to be one. And, by the way, we are all on that continuum. The Change Equation, if necessary, psycho-dynamically validates whoever you are.

Sublimate

You are what you are. You can change your personality liabilities, or you can sublimate them. Sublimation, by the way, is too a change. The kind of change that does not toss the baby's character out with the water. The Change Equation does not try to undo what has been already done, it offers to sublimate it.

If, as a narcissist, you want exclusivity, a sense of superiority, and power, go ahead and try the seemingly impossible: quit using, do it better and faster than anyone, do it now. If, as an obsessive-compulsive, you want to control, start by controlling yourself, your cravings, your maladaptive thoughts, and your interpersonal demeanor. If, as an antisocial, you want to cut corners and manipulate others, how about pushing cars instead of drugs, or manipulating managerially rather than criminally. If, as an avoidant, you wish to escape, pick a better way to Nirvana than a bottle of Scotch that creates unnecessary interpersonal encounters with confrontational family members, judges in the courtrooms, and cellmates in the jail.

While many therapeutic approaches, particularly, of psycho-dynamic orientation, validate and educate clients about their psychological nature, they also eventually propose modifications. The Change Equation offers psycho-analytical education by pointing out that a person does not have to change who they are, they can do just fine by finding a better use for their psychological idiosyncrasies. In short, if you are a hammer, stop banging on china, find yourself a nail. If you are an avoidant, stop hiding in the bottle, find a monastery and maybe you will be canonized.

Motivate/Inoculate

This principle conveys a dialectic clinical stance that, on one hand, intrinsically motivates the client for change, and, on the other hand, inoculates the client to any extrinsic changes in circumstance.

Motivate

Why do you want to change? Why do you want to stop drinking or drugging? The chances are that today's first reason will be tomorrow's last reason on the list.

How can I assert that? Most people are uncomfortable with being selfish; therefore, their reasons for change are typically extrinsic. They want to change for someone else. They do not want to embarrass their families or spouses. They do not want to model unacceptable behavior to their children. They want to go to treatment so that they can get out of jail sooner, and, in doing so, go to treatment for the judge, not themselves.

The trouble is that extrinsic motivation does not exist. Whatever a person does, he or she benefits from it one way or another. There are always psychological kicks to be had, be it from writing this very sentence or making an anonymous donation to a charity. Extrinsic motivation is but an intrinsic motivation that, to an outsider, appears as altruism. By seemingly wasting my time in helping an older lady cross the street, I invest a major coin in the piggy-bank of my self-worth. Amazingly, what happens inside us is harder for us to see than it is for other people. Our moralizing superegos forget that they are at the service of our Ids. But wait a second: what does all of this have to do with change?! Everything. To clarify, nothing is possible without an intrinsic motivation. Intrinsic motivation is primordial in its effectiveness. Extrinsic motivation is nothing but motivational self-sabotage.

The problem, however, is that while extrinsic motivation does not really exist, the illusion of extrinsic motivation does exist and frequently sabotages change. As we embark on a process of change (such as quitting drug use) we often, though not always, do it to appease our significant others or to get the legal system off our back.

This is a wrong way to go. The Change Equation aims to enhance motivation for change by encouraging a crystallization of a reason to change that can withstand any change in circumstance. A person quitting heroin use is expected to find a reason to quit heroin use that would still apply if heroin were legalized the moment he leaves the rehab. Such enduring reasons are surprisingly easy to find.

Allow me to share a brief vignette to illustrate the utility of intrinsic motivation.

A client of mine that had been shot and stabbed as part of his "street" career struggled to find a powerful intrinsic motivation. In exploring his concerns about old debts catching up with him when he hits the bricks, he realized that if he were to find himself at gun-point (one more time in his life) he wants to be able to really mean it when he says, "Fuck you!" The client's realization was in part predicated on his prior understanding that when you are under the influence, you are really not you, therefore, whatever you say, you cannot really mean it, since, in a way, you, as a psychological entity, are not really there to begin with.

While hardly a motivation for the judge's ears, this motivation is a good intrinsic reason to stop using drugs. But as good and useful as this intrinsic motivation sounds, it is far from perfect. We will revisit its flaws in just a moment.

Inoculate

What is inoculation? Inoculation introduces an organism to a threat with the purpose of hardening the organism. A real or symbolic threat teaches the person a survival response, and, is, therefore, an invaluable tool of adaptation.

Aside from such biological inoculation as vaccination, there exist various forms of psychological inoculation. Teasing and tickling, for example, are more than just obnoxious pastimes. These activities train a child how to spar verbally and physically. The Change Equation utilizes this researched but underutilized psychological technology to harden clients' motivations for change.

To illustrate this, allow me to return to the example with the correctional client.

As my client shared his desire to really mean it when he says, "Fuck you!" if he were to find himself at gun-point again, I questioned whether this motivation could withstand any circumstance. First off, I asked what would keep the client clean if he does not find himself at gun-point. He acknowledged that he could not realistically count on such an event. He promptly and with savvy, dug deeper. He explained that he wants to really mean it, whenever he says that phrase. He explained that those kinds of words should not be said lightly and should be meant. I agreed and continued to inoculate. "What if you have no reason to say these words? What if you cannot speak?" My follow-up questions obviously annoyed him (a sign of effective inoculation in progress). After a pause, he nailed it right on the head. "I want to be able to mean everything I think," were his words. This, by all measures, was one of the best intrinsic motivations I had heard in a while. "When I am high," he added, touching his temple with his index finger, "I cannot think or mean my thoughts." I rested my case. My client developed a desire to be the Thinker behind his thoughts, i.e. an intrinsic motivation that can withstand any extrinsic change in circumstance.

As evident from this example, inoculation cuts away the situational fluff of a proposed reason to change and helps the client tap into a broader underlying principle which leads to a motivation that endures any situational change. Therefore, effective motivating cannot occur without effective inoculating. Most of the traditional substance use treatments are leery about playing too much devil's advocacy. The Change Equation method, however, views this as a key treatment principle. With this in mind, the key motivational goal of the Change Equation method is to first, motivate the client to find a no-matter-what motivation, to prevent the client from self-sabotage, then, to assist him in finding an unconditional reason for change, and finally, to inoculate the client to any motivational sabotage that he or she may encounter in the future.

Catastrophize/Decatastrophize

This principle conveys a dialectic clinical stance that, on one hand, teaches the client to prevent the initial using episode by catastrophizing the negative consequence of the use, and, on the other hand, prevents the further using episode by teaching the client to de-catastrophize the negative consequences of the using episode that had already taken place.

Despite a long-standing clinical literature detailing the process of abstinence violation, the distinction between a lapse and a relapse continues to be more of a theoretical construct than an empirical tool in use prevention treatments. While there is more to lapse prevention than catastrophizing, and more to relapse prevention than decatastrophizing, the Change Equation utilizes the Catastrophize/Decatastrophize treatment guideline as a mnemonic that can be used to govern clinicians involved in the day-to-day interaction with clients in treatment.

Catastrophizing (subtle, not tongue-in-cheek) is, therefore, conceptualized as a motivational intervention. The Change Equation facilitators remain attuned to any opportunities to enhance clients' motivation to avoid engaging in the target behavior. At the same time, in the event that a client did lapse, the Change Equation facilitators are expected to be prepared to help the client decatastrophize the occurrence to assist the client in getting back on the proverbial wagon.

The Catastrophize/Decatastrophize principle is particularly intended for residential aftercare. At present, many of the residential aftercare entities (such as half-way houses or three-quarter houses) are quick to kick out the resident for having a lapse. The official rationale for such an unforgiving stance is that one resident's lapse threatens the entire community. Administrators often remark that they are hesitant to take a person who lapsed back because they do not want to communicate to the rest of the residents that lapsing is ok. This, of course, in itself, is a form of catastrophizing. One person's mistake does not sanction or necessitate others' mistakes. To think otherwise is to deny one's clients the benefit of common sense.

Consequently, the traditional aftercare entities are often good at catastrophizing before the lapse and after it. The obvious problem with this is that while catastrophizing before the lapse might prevent a using episode, catastrophizing after the first using episode ensures the second. A person in recovery is therefore left stranded and without support. The initial lapse becomes the relapse, and that, in its turn, reinforces the vicious cycle of the belief that substance use is a relapsing disease. This scare tactic, of course, keeps residential aftercare entities in demand and the entire Recovery Industry happily employed. As the Recovery Industry churns out more disease, the society at large embraces the permissive determinism of addiction. That, in its turn, leads to the demise of the entire civilization as people abandon their belief in choice. And that, of course, heralds the end of the world, as we know it. The end of the world, of course, affects me, you, and everybody, and all of this because of the action of one unfortunate…

But wait a second! I think I might be catastrophizing here. See, catastrophizing is not always good, didn't I tell you?

De-Automatize/Re-Automatize

This principle conveys a dialectic clinical stance that, on one hand, prompts the client to de-automatize an observed and previously unconscious schematic/autopiloted/habitual behavior, and, on the other hand, prompts the client to re-automatize the de-automatized behavior by an act of conscious choice.

De-Automatize

Humans, functionally, are automatons that forget that they are automatons. Asking an automaton to de-automatize is therapeutic. It allows the human who acts like an automaton to appreciate that he does not have to act like an automaton.

Re-Automatize

Humans, albeit capable of de-automatization, require re-automatization to function. If I ask you right now to de-automatize your reading, you will stop reading. And, indeed, allow yourself to become consciously aware of the position of your head, of the movement of your eyes, of the grasp of your hands on the sides of the book. There you go. Actually, there you stop.

So we have a problem. You have de-automatized your reading, probably still somewhat self-observant, even right now, and, as a result, somewhat distracted. It is good since you, I presume, are experiencing de-automatization, even as you read, but, on the other hand, I would like for you to finish reading my book.

In respecting the fact that you need to re-automatize in order to continue reading, I ask you to do it in a way that might be somewhat unfamiliar to you. The classic way to re-automatize a given behavior is to just do it, whatever that might phenomenologically mean. That "just doing it" might be triggered by the first step in the behavioral sequence, for example. Just letting this re-automatization happen, however, denies you a precedent of choice. If, for example, you struggle with any kind of compulsive behaviors, this precedent of choice about something as automatic as reading, might be of particular experiential value. So, without further ado, allow yourself to first de-automatize and, then, when you are ready, allow yourself to re-automatize, but instead of just letting it happen, allow yourself a conscious thought that you are choosing to re-automatize, that you have a choice about when to re-automatize and whether to re-automatize at all. Go ahead; play with your head.

Welcome back (if you left, of course). By the way, any kind of parenthetical statement of the sort I just made is a fleeting moment of de-automatizing. What did I de-automatize, you might wonder. When I wrote, "welcome back," I realized that those words automatically imply that you had left, an assumption I cannot verify. Since I am interested in being fair to both the reader that played along and the one that did not, I had to de-automatize. And now, realizing that I am rambling, I am de-automatizing my rambling, and making a conscious choice (hold on a second) to re-automatize to being relevant and to the point.

The Change Equation allots much emphasis to the so-called Choice Awareness Training that is followed up with Choice Awareness Practice. Much of choice awareness training and practice might sound very similar to what happened on the preceding page. The point of this treatment principle and its discussion here is not to preview Choice Awareness Training, but to introduce a particular clinical stance that I utilize in the work with my clients.

Consequently, the De-Automatize/Re-Automatize principle describes a type of here-and-now processing that I throw into a session as I please, both to help clients appreciate the freedom-asserting value of Choice Awareness, and to enhance the quality of clinical interaction at any given time.

Logotherapy & Substance Use Treatment

Somov, P.G. (2007). Meaning of Life Group: Group Application of Logotherapy for Substance Use Treatment. Journal for Specialists in Group Work, 32 (4), 316 - 345.

Abstract

The rationale for the use of logotherapy in the context of substance use treatment is introduced. The article reviews prior group applications of logotherapy and offers a clinical curriculum for a group application of logotherapy tailored to the substance use treatment context. Furthermore, the article provides a discussion of the specifics of the group format and role induction to the "Meaning of Life" group, as well as a detailed discussion of eight themes that constitute the proposed logotherapeutic group intervention for substance use population.

Logotherapy, a meaning-oriented therapy developed by Victor Frankl (1955) as an individual therapy modality is, in its pure form, a comparatively rare therapy of choice in contemporary clinical practice. Logotherapy as a group modality is even more rare.

Joseph Fabry (1988), in his book Guideposts of Meaning: Discovering What Really Matters, suggests that despite its fundamentally personal nature logotherapy is, in fact, suitable for a group format. A few "sharing" groups have been developed and described by logotherapists over time. Fabry's own "Finding Meaning Every Day" group protocol is a better known group application of logotherapy and is designed to provide clients "with tools for restructuring their lives in ways that are meaningful to them, so that their daily behavior more nearly expresses their values" (1988, p. 123).

While logotherapy authors such as Lukas (1979) and Crumbaugh (1979) wrote about the application of logotherapy to substance use treatment, a structured logotherapy group that is thematically tailored for the substance use treatment setting, has not, to the knowledge of this author, been proposed until Somov and Somova (2003). The present article introduces the Meaning of Life group protocol as a motivation-enhancing and relapse-prevention application of logotherapy for substance use treatment.

Rationale for Using Logotherapy in the Context of Substance Use
Treatment

In delineating the scope and goals of logotherapy, Frankl (1955)
juxtaposed it with psychoanalysis by defining it as "existential analysis" that "seeks to bring to awareness the concepts of the mind," in the
goal of helping the client "toward the consciousness of responsibility"
as "being responsible is one of the essential grounds of human existence" (1955, p. 29). Existential review, search for meaning, and
assuming responsibility are pivotal to the substance use recovery arc.
Recovery, in itself, is not a goal, but a means to a goal, a means to
facilitating a meaningful life. Consequently, the Meaning of Life Group
is an attempt to help clients place their substance use in the existential
context. Lukas (1979) notes that upon completion of treatment, substance use clients are likely to "ask themselves if there was any sense of
their being cured and what they will do with the life that was restored
to them" (p. 263). Indeed, a person coming out of an otherwise successful rehabilitation may ask of him or herself, "Ok, so I got clean…
Now what?!" Leaving this question unanswered seems to be an
invitation to relapse. While incentive-based motivations can help a
client initiate a change, a meaning-based motivation may assure the
maintenance of clinical gains. Consequently, clients are invited to start
the recovery process by taking a look beyond the recovery, beyond the
myopia of "getting back on track," towards the destination of the life-
track. This is accomplished by priming clients' consciousness with the

"meaning of life" questions, i.e. existential and philosophical questions that allow clients to broaden their motivational search from short-lived, tactical, and often cliché motivations to person-specific, meaning-centered motivations that serve as a buffer against the turbulence of change.

Logotherapy can help normalize the angst of recovery as a normal existential "vital sign." When clients are asked to ponder the interplay between meaninglessness (the all too familiar feelings of emptiness) and substance use, they are offered a normalizing, de-pathologized perspective on substance use as an escape from meaninglessness and a legitimate albeit sub-optimal form of trying to resolve noogenic neurosis or noogenic depression (Frankl, 1978). As such, the Meaning of Life Group introduces validating existential language into motivational enhancement that frees the client from the paralysis of self-deprecating guilt and refocuses the client on regaining meaning through recovery.

The Meaning of Life group protocol attempts to awaken the philosopher inside a given client, providing a substance use client with an opportunity to strategically zoom out, to reset his or her existential compass, to place both substance abuse/misuse and recovery in the trajectory of one's life journey, to resuscitate the anesthetized and deadened will-to-meaning in the hope of giving recovery more than tactical importance. As such, logotherapy in the context of substance use treatment not only facilitates motivation for change but also serves as an important lapse/relapse prevention factor. There is more to life than recovery. Recovery is but a means to an end, not an end in and of itself. Clients for whom recovery becomes an end in and of itself are at added risk for relapse should they lapse in the first place. And, indeed, if being in recovery has become a defining part of one's narrative, if recovery has become an end in and of itself, catastrophizing interpretations of a lapse (as an end of everything that matters) are inevitable, and so is a relapse.

This can be best understood in terms of Linville's (1985) research on self-complexity. Linville (1985) suggests that narrowly defined self-concepts are less stable than self-concepts that consist of multiple roles that are well differentiated from each other. Metaphorically, stable self-concepts are like submarines that are buffered from sinking by the fact that they consist of multiple hermetically separated compartments which isolate a leak in a given compartment from the rest of the submarine, allowing even a damaged, leaking submarine to remain afloat. A person in recovery whose life consists of multiple well-differentiated meanings, for whom recovery is but one of several means to a particular life-goal, would appear to be better buffered from stress and psychological "sinking" than a person in recovery who has turned recovery into a life-long cause and found a life's meaning in staying "clean." Life-long recovery-oriented socialization, life-long self-definition as an "addict" or as always "recovering" or through "years clean," or excessive enmeshment of recovery and spirituality, run the risk of a single-track self-concept with recovery turned into a life's meaning. When the treatment goal of recovery becomes a life goal, little leaks (lapses) become gushing catastrophic floods (relapses). Consequently, logotherapy, in addition to priming and enhancing motivation for change, can be invaluable in relapse prevention by helping substance use clients not substitute a narrow self-concept of an "addict" with a similarly narrow self-concept of being "a recovering addict."

Meaning of Life Group Format

The Meaning of Life Group is a professionally-facilitated, secular, content-based, structured group that raises questions, facilitates a non-judgmental discussion of various issues of existential significance, and involves various experiential exercises. While the content is philosophical in nature, intellectualizing is discouraged. Facilitators follow the method of Socratic inquiry, a discourse method of preference in logotherapy, the goal of which is not "to pour information into the students, but rather to elicit from the students what they already know intuitively" (Fabry, 1988, p. 9). In this process, facilitators are encouraged to remain attuned to what Fabry referred to as "logohints," or phrases, facial expressions, intonations that indicate "what is meaningful to the seeker," clues to clients' "positive attitudes and values" (1988, p. 12). Furthermore, facilitators do not educate but facilitate clients' self-discovery; facilitators do not provide meaning but point out "meaning possibilities" (Fabry et al, 1979, p. 265). As noted by Lukas (1979), the final responsibility for the found meanings and their implications rests with the clients.

Facilitators remain mindful of the natural interplay between meaning and spirituality, but avoid direct discussion of religious topics,

redirect clients' from direct questioning of fellow group members'
religious pronouncements and defer direct discussions of religious
beliefs to more appropriate non-secular forums. The facilitators, of
course, avoid imposing their values or endorsing others' values with the
emphasis of the group being on raising the questions, rather than on
answering them. Facilitators explicitly recognize and help clients
recognize that while there might be the question, there isn't always the
answer.

Client Role Induction/Group Rules

At the outset of the group, the facilitator delineates the following
parameters and group rules: a) Meaning of Life group is an opportunity
to discuss the meaning of life and how it relates to substance use and
recovery; b) group members will express opinions and avoid imposing
or "pitching" their beliefs to others; c) group members will attempt to
remain open to exploration of the life implications of the opinions they
express; d) specific religious questions or religious opinions are best
reserved for spiritual counseling and are not appropriate for this forum;
e) group members will exercise respect and tact in relating to each
other; f) no self-disclosure is required to participate, silence is accepted.
The facilitator explicitly positions him or herself as a person with
questions, not answers.

The Eight Theme Curriculum

Frankl (1955), discussing the scope of logotherapy as existential analysis, emphasizes the exploration of meaning of life, meaning of death, meaning of suffering, meaning of work, and meaning of love.

The following are eight discussion themes that structure the curriculum of the Meaning of Life group:

Theme 1:	Meaning of Meaninglessness
Theme 2:	Meaning of Adversity
Theme 3:	Meaning of Self
Theme 4:	Meaning of Presence
Theme 5:	Meaning of Death
Theme 6:	Meaning of Freedom
Theme 7:	Meaning of Substance Use
Theme 8:	Meaning of Transition

The reader should be aware that the theme content presented in this article differs from the original Meaning of Life group theme curriculum, as described in The Recovery Equation: Motivational Enhancement, Choice Awareness, Use Prevention, an Innovative Clinical Curriculum for Substance Use Treatment" (Somov & Somova, 2003). The original Meaning of Life group did not include the discussion of the meaning of freedom as this topic was addressed through a stand-alone Choice Awareness Training treatment module.

Theme 1 – Role Induction and the Meaning of Meaninglessness

The first session pursues three tasks: to provide role induction for the group, to normalize meaninglessness, and to facilitate positive expectations regarding the relevance of the group to clients' recovery efforts. The role induction into the Meaning of Life group begins with a description of the rationale for the group and the presentation of the group rules. The five core existential questions may be briefly presented to stimulate interest and engagement. The other key ideas at this point are as follows: a) search for meaning aids in search for motivation for recovery, b) recovery, while a treatment goal, is not a life goal per se, recovery is a means to end, not an end in and of itself, c) substance use is normalized and humanized as an understandable but problematic search for meaning, for some, and, for others, as an understandable, albeit problematic, form of coping with meaninglessness. In presenting the rationale and the ideas above, the facilitators model a contemplative, non-judgmental atmosphere, and reinforce the idea that philosophizing, i.e. thinking about meaning of life, is not a luxury but a necessity.

       To further set the mood for the group, group members might be asked to recall times when they gazed at the stars. In eliciting clients' accounts, star-gazing, as an experience, is recognized as an attempt to somehow integrate one's life with the seductively overwhelming universe outside, as a moment of self-transcendence. Clients are also asked to recall if after an episode of star-gazing, they felt an inspired, motivated eagerness to change, to somehow bring their life in order with their realizations. Star-gazing can be also offered as a metaphor of navigation or finding the way for those who might feel lost or without direction. The answers to the meaning-of-life questions presented in this group can be metaphorically likened to constellations of meaning that help clients navigate towards their life-goals and, at times of confusion, to re-assess their existential coordinates.

A key task of the first session is to normalize clients' sense of meaninglessness. While facilitators are encouraged to normalize meaninglessness throughout this intervention, the first session aims to explicitly de-pathologize clients' possible feelings of emptiness and meaninglessness. The search for meaning is recognized as work in progress, as a kind of existential hypothesis-testing in which people try out different models of meaning in search of the best existential fit. Consequently, lack of meaning, lack of answers to life's fundamental questions is hardly evidence of a deficit of wisdom but, if anything, a reflection of the complexity of questions posed.

Theme 2 – Meaning of Adversity: What is the meaning of pain and suffering?

Frequently, admission to substance use treatment is precipitated by adversity. Making sense of adversity, therefore, taps into the most immediate phenomenology of a person in treatment and serves as an emotionally validating, meaning-finding and motivation enhancing opportunity. Making sense of random adversity and adversity that resulted from clients' failures can help clients see that their suffering

had not been all in vein. In the words of Elizabeth Lukas, a logotherapeutic approach allows "failures become retrospectively filled with
meaning" (Fabry et al, 1979).

   Coping versus Meaning Focused Suffering. Coping is designed
to reduce suffering. Coping literature distinguishes two approaches to
reducing suffering: problem focused and emotion focused coping
(Folkman, 1984). Problem focused coping reduces suffering through
behavioral problem-solving. Emotion focused coping aims to reduce
suffering by controlling and suppressing the corresponding negative
emotionality.

   Both problem focused and emotion focused coping strategies
represent an attempt to solve a problem, either through a behavioral or
attitudinal solution. In achieving that both of these coping approaches
appear tactical and neglect the bigger picture, that of the existential
meaning of having a problem in the first place. Meaning focused
suffering, while akin to coping, does not automatically view a given
problem as a problem; instead, meaning focused suffering attempts to
place a given problematic event or occurrence that had resulted in
suffering in a broader existential context. Depending on a person's
particular existential interpretation of meaning, a person may reject the
idea of suffering as a problem altogether and see the fact of a problem
not as a problem per se but as a "vital sign" of life or a consequence of
his or her freely made choice. Consequently, meaning focused suffering does not replace problem-solving (or solution focused) coping but
compliments it by viewing suffering as an opportunity to manifest
attitudinal values.

Facilitating Meaning Focused Suffering. In developing the Meaning of
Suffering theme, the facilitators may briefly introduce the distinction
between problem focused and emotion focused coping, as a prelude to
a discussion of the meaning focused suffering. Following this, facilitators open discussion with a question along the lines of: "What do you
think is the meaning of suffering, pain, adversity, hard times?" The
discussion may result in a variety of meaning-focused interpretations of
suffering. The following is a summary of common existential interpretations of suffering.

Adversity as Contrast:

Pain and suffering create contrast for happiness and well-being.
You can't know pleasure without knowing pain.

Adversity as a Normal Part of Life:

Adversity is a normal, unavoidable, part of the human experience.
Pain is a vital sign, a sign that we are alive.

Adversity as a Learning/Growth Opportunity:

No pain, no gain.
There is a silver lining (an opportunity for growth) to every cloud
(adversity).

Adversity as Consequence and Manifestation of Our Freedom:

Adversity is an occasional consequence of our choices.

Adversity is an occasional cost of our freedom.

Adversity as Punishment or Misfortune:

Adversity is punishment and penance.

Adversity is a result of misfortune and bad luck

Adversity as Preparation and Inoculation for Greater Adversity:

What doesn't kill us, makes us stronger.

Coping with adversity is a skill, adversity is an opportunity to practice coping.

Suffering Focus and Substance Use Interplay.

To consolidate the theme of Meaning of Adversity facilitators are advised to invite clients to examine the interplay between the suffering focus and substance use episodes. For example, problem-focused suffering may catastrophize suffering as intolerable and unacceptable and, therefore, can lead to chemical coping. Solution-focused coping also views adversity as a problem and may guide a person to cope with pain and suffering by escaping into substance use. Meaning-focused suffering may reject the view of suffering as a problem altogether and see the fact of having a problem, at a minimum, as a normal part of life, and, at a maximum, as an opportunity to manifest one's life-values.

The Suffering Vice-Grip Exercise.

In his book The Doctor and the Soul, Frankl talks of "squeezing" meaning out of suffering (p. 300, 1955). The facilitator introduces the notion of "squeezing meaning out of suffering." Facilitators may offer a metaphor of an existential vice-grip that wrings the meaning out of suffering. Clients are asked to think of instances of suffering in recent past and to put them, metaphorically, through the Suffering Vice-Grip to squeeze out the meaning.

Theme 3 – Meaning of Self: Who/What am I?

"Who/What am I?", as a question of great ambiguity, is a litmus test of a person's tolerance of existential discourse. Therefore, to leverage group participants' interest in this seemingly impractical question, the facilitator would do well to begin by inviting group members to explore the possible utility of knowing who/what they are in the context of their recovery. This initial approach to the topic is a good opportunity to reiterate the view of recovery as a means to an end rather than a goal in and of itself. The key point of the current theme is to broaden clients' view of themselves beyond their often narrow view of themselves as an "addict" or a "recovering addict." This can be accomplished by the examination of who/what clients were prior to their substance use as well as by encouraging clients to consider who/what they are aside from their substance use and aside from their recovery ("You say you are an addict, or a recovering addict, okay... and aside from that, what else are you? What else can you say about who you are? What makes you you?").

Exploring Addiction Self-Definitions.

Clients in substance use treatment frequently define themselves as "addicts" or "recovering addicts/alcoholics." Exploring these treatment-endorsed self-definitions as well as such derogatory addiction slang terms as "junkie," "crack-head," "pot-head" allows clients to evaluate the impact of these self-conceptualizations on their self-esteem and recovery potential. More specifically, clients are asked : "When you call yourself an addict, what does that mean? What is the meaning of you saying that you are always going to be a recovering alcoholic?" Facilitators may also offer clients to evaluate and compare such alternative addiction self-definition alternatives as "habitual substance user" or "chemical coper."

Finding Self through Past.

Fabry (1988) recommends examination of one's family history as a means to finding meaning in everyday living. Consequently, inviting clients to explore their family history might be useful in helping clients appreciate where they came from and where they are going. Exploration of one's roots may help clients feel connected and grounded in the past, and to see their role and responsibilities in the trans-generational transmission of family values and traditions.

Value Hierarchy.

Assessment of one's values may also prove a useful tool in the search for the meaning of "who I am." Fabry (1988) offers a formalized assessment of one's value hierarchy that allows clients to track the actual origin of their values by source (family, society, self, etc.). Such value assessment can help clients also explore the extent to which who they are is a product of cultural, familial programming, and to what extent who they are is a function of their own values and philosophy of living.

Highlighting the Discrepancy between the Real and Ideal Self.
As the clients explore the meaning of who they are, they might be also encouraged to evaluate the degree of correspondence between who they actually are (Real Self) at the present time against who they aspire to be (Ideal Self). This juxtaposition between the Real and the Ideal Selves creates a state of cognitive dissonance similar to what Saunders et al. (1991) term as a psychological squirm, a state that further facilitates motivation for change.

Theme 4 – Meaning of Presence

The emotional parcel of this theme is to awaken a sense of appreciation for being alive, right now. The goal is to try to facilitate emergence of a sense of urgency (and even angst) about the need to at least pose and ponder existential questions, in order not to miss the opportunity for meaning. The primary method of the session is that of infusing an awareness of time. In my experience, any discussion of existential issues without the psychological "squirm" of time awareness is likely to remain a purely intellectual exercise. Infusing a here-and-now awareness of time passing into the discussion of the existential issues sets a tone for an affectively-laden and, therefore, motivationally-priming and personally-relevant experience.

On a technical note, the facilitators arrive for the session with an hour glass and offer a pensive opening: "The sand of time... clocks ticking... moments passing... as I sleep, as I go to work, as I sit in the traffic jam... time's passing... life's passing... someone's dying... someone's just being born..." The facilitator waits in silence, allowing the metaphor and the imagery to take hold. He or she then continues: "You are alive right now... by historical standards, you will be gone in a flash of time... What does it mean to you to be alive right now, in this moment, a moment after so many have already died, and a moment before so many are yet to be born?"

Following this "contemplative narrative," the facilitator defers to the group for thoughts and reactions. The facilitator "moves" the process by re-infusing the awareness of time whenever the sand of time runs out: "right now, in this very moment, someone's life is coming to an end, they might or might not know it, their clock is about to stop... and someone's life just beginning... what does that mean to you, right now?"

Facilitators wrap up the session by checking for feelings. Feelings of urgency, restlessness, desire to be productive are not uncommon. Facilitators may validate this yearning "to do something" as a common ('manic") defense against concerns of mortality and may encourage clients to stay with the restlessness, to not rush to do something, but to wait and explore opportunities for meaning that become more apparent when the blurring and dizzying carousel of escapist behavior slows down and the confusion of not-knowing paradoxically offers moments of clarity.

Facilitators aim to leave some time for appreciating life as it is happening right now for each and every group member in the room. They offer gentle guidance: "This is it... right now, this is your life... passing... are you present?" The facilitator should be prepared that some clients will find this invitation for mindful presence as a gift, while others, feeling the "squirm" of mindfulness, may resist such an invitation by whispering or giggling.

Theme 5 – Meaning of Death: Where am I going?

Meaning of life and meaning of death are intertwined. Our beliefs about death define our approach to living. The "meaning of death" question, however, is often a surprise to the non-philosophizing public. Facilitators, prepared for this surprise, simply ask: "What is the meaning of death? What does death mean to you? What are your beliefs about death? What do you think happens next, after you die, if anything? If life is a journey, where do you believe you are going? What do you believe to be the destination of this journey that we call life?" The answers to the "meaning of death" question is likely to reveal clients' religious beliefs. With this in mind, it is important to avoid any evaluation of the expressed beliefs. Therefore, for example, facilitators are encouraged to avoid such probes as "What do others think about what so-and-so said?" Having done this existential "roll-call" on the issue of death, facilitators summarize the stated themes and offer a discussion of the interplay between clients' beliefs about death and their substance use.

Destination: Somewhere vs. Nowhere.

Some people view life as a prelude to after-life, while others see life as containing no destination other than death, and, thus, being a destination unto itself. In my experience, the difference on this point has the potential of being quite emotionally divisive. Consequently, in helping clients explore their beliefs about the meaning of death, facilitators have to be on their "process" toes to minimize any aggression in debate. The facilitators should be prepared to understand and summarize the following three common perspectives on death: 1) death as the beginning of an after-life, 2) death as the ultimate end of life, and 3) death as rebirth (reincarnation). Naturally, the facilitators may also run into an agnostic perspective of "not knowing" what death means, which could be then constructed as death as an unknown.

Substance use as Transcendence.

The recovery "business" is often a judgmental business. The humanity of substance use, with its ancient roots in various world cultures, is, unfortunately, under-recognized and moralizing abounds. The Meaning of Life group facilitators should be prepared to recognize and validate a view of substance use as a spiritual search for transcendence. To clarify, validation is not an expression of values about a given position or an endorsement of a particular position. Validation is acceptance of the phenomenological logic of a given position. Being clear on this point allows Meaning of Life group facilitators to offer their clients a rare opportunity not to "demonize" their substance use but to openly reminisce about its existential value. On a practical note, the sub-theme of substance use as transcendence can be facilitated by such questions as: "How has substance use changed your attitude to death, if at all?" or "In what ways, if at all, has substance use helped you resolve your fears or questions about death?"

Death as Discontinuity of Self.

Beliefs about death are also intertwined with the idea of continuity of "I-ness" or continuity of self. This seemingly heavy-duty philosophical angle can be introduced with relative ease along the following lines: "Some people suggest that you are your consciousness... With this in mind, are such states as sleep/unconsciousness/coma a form of psychological death?" The idea here is to look at death from the stand-point

of loss of sense of self or self-control such as in the case of unconscious
or substance-induced behavior. In this context, life then could be
defined as "being awake, being conscious, being your usual self," and
death as "being asleep, unconscious (as in coma), not your usual self."
Extending this idea further, facilitators may explore the idea of being
intoxicated or under the influence as a temporary death/cessation of
one's usual self ("When you are high, are you you?"). The overall
vector of this sub-theme is to explore the perspective of substance use
from the stand-point of temporary loss of selves. While for some this
idea might appear too esoteric, for others it may lead to an insight that
if life means being awake, and death means sleep, then extreme states
of intoxication may, in fact, represent a loss of conscious, a loss of self,
i.e. a loss of life that is, therefore, to be mourned. To further facilitate
this discussion, therapists may simply inquire: "In what ways is substance use similar to death?" In my experience, this particular sub-
theme is a clinical Klondike of potentially motivating insights.

Substance Use as "Reversible" Death.

Most substance use treatment providers are familiar with the escapist,
avoidant, if not para-suicidal function of substance use. Some individuals, at times of adversity, consciously look for a means to "numb
out," to escape pain and suffering, and, not uncommonly, to escape
themselves. Drugging and drinking as a "reversible suicide," as an
escape from one's self is a likely theme to come up in the context of the
discussion of the meaning of death.

Death and Dying.

In discussing the meaning of death, facilitators should be prepared to encounter a theme of grief and loss. Direct elicitation of this sub-theme is not recommended since grief-related disclosures are likely to monopolize group time. Therefore, facilitators should be prepared to redirect client's disclosures about their grief. This can be accomplished by acknowledging the comment and broadening the scope of potential reply by inviting the group to relate. For example, the facilitator may say: "Jake here mentioned about losing his Mom, about how painful and hard that was... I am sure many of you in the group have had similarly painful losses. How do you think these deaths changed your beliefs about death? What do you think these deaths had to do with your substance use?"

Theme 6 - Meaning of Freedom: Am I free?

Meaning of freedom is one of the pivotal existential questions for anyone and, particularly, for anyone embarking on substance use recovery. "Am I free or is everything predetermined?" – the answer to this question often determines the client's conceptual map of recovery. The current theme is designed to approach the issue of freedom in a concentrically-focusing manner, beginning at a broader level of abstraction, gradually zooming in on the personal and practical implications of one's beliefs about the issue of freedom, with an eventual close-up on how beliefs about freedom interface with one's approach to recovery.

Philosophical Level of Abstraction.

Facilitators introduce the topic at the broadest level of abstraction by simply asking: "What is freedom?" The discussion can be further enhanced by the introduction of the distinction between freedom and determinism. Facilitators may, for example, introduce such a "truism" as the idea that "everything has a cause" and then challenge clients to try to reconcile the seemingly deterministic causality of everything that happens with the phenomenologically convincing sense of freedom of choice. Clients might be further stimulated by such probes as: "What are your thoughts about the notions of destiny, fate, or a Grand Plan?" Clients might be also offered the distinction between hard determinism and soft determinism (predisposition for a particular course of action with an option of volitional override). For example, facilitators may offer an example of someone with a so-called "short fuse," who, under usual circumstances, might be "easy to fire up," but who is, neverthe-less, able to manage their anger much better, say, at a gun point, or during an important job interview with much at stake. Such a discus-sion can help clients tease out the distinction between causes, predispo-sitions, and actual behavioral choices. This particular sub-theme can be further consolidated by offering a definition of freedom as awareness of options available to an individual at any given point (Somov & So-mova, 2003).

Ethico-Practical Level of Abstraction.

At this level of abstraction, facilitators shift the discussion towards ethical and practical implications of client's beliefs about freedom. This is accomplished by asking clients about the interrelationship between "freedom" and "responsibility." More specifically, facilitators inquire along the following lines: "This is a question to those of you who believe that everything has a cause and that your current behavior is predetermined by your prior actions and behaviors... If what you are right now is a function of who you were yesterday and so and so forth, then, how can you be held responsible for what you are doing at any given point?" Additionally, the facilitators explore the ethico-pragmatic implications of clients' beliefs about the interplay between socio-economic factors and problems of poverty, violence or substance use. In conclusion of this sub-theme about freedom and responsibility, the facilitators may offer the following two perspectives: a) if you believe that everything is pre-determined, then you belief you are not free, and, therefore, you are not responsible for what you do (even though the society and the legal system will hold you responsible for your actions); and b) if you believe you are fundamentally free, despite any bio-psycho-social predispositions you might have, you are also ultimately responsible, with responsibility being the cost of your freedom.

Personal/Substance-Use Level of Abstraction.

As with any discussion, progressing from philosophical to personal tends to be accompanied by the risk of increased emotionality which is in proportion to insecurity of our beliefs. One such belief that lies at the core of the existential notion of freedom and responsibility, is the belief that addiction is a disease. Facilitators are cautioned to tread carefully around this issue as mere questioning of the disease model of addiction is tantamount to "sacrilege" in certain substance use settings. Yet, the issue of whether substance use and dependence is, indeed, a disease, in a technical, rather than metaphorical, sense is a bone fide existential issue. Prior to embarking on this subject, facilitators are encouraged to do preliminary readings on the history of the disease model of addiction (Jellinek, 1972) as well as of the criticism of conceptualizing substance use as a disease (Peele, 1999). Viewing addiction as a disease is a form of determinism which makes one no more responsible for the disease of addiction than for the disease of cancer. Conceptualizing substance use as a habit represents a form of "soft determinism" that views substance use as a behavioral predisposition (reflective of past behavioral choice and conditioning) that is, nevertheless, subject to volitional control.

Eliciting these distinctions from clients can be accomplished by such questions as: "What is a disease? What are some examples of diseases? Are you responsible for, say, having cancer? Are you free to not have cancer by merely choosing not to have it? Is addiction a disease? What does viewing addiction as disease mean to you about your responsibility for substance use? What does viewing addiction as a disease mean to you about whether you are free to recover from it? What is the difference in viewing substance use as a disease versus viewing it as a habit? Are you free to choose to not act in accordance with your habitual inclinations and your habitual predispositions?" Challenging clients to evaluate the interplay between their beliefs about freedom and responsibility and their model of addiction is one of the key guideposts to meaning on the path to recovery.

Theme 7 – Meaning of Substance Use: What does drinking/drugging do for us?

The process of change cannot begin with a conviction that one is irrational. Substance use is not evidence of irrationality but is merely evidence of a person's search for an optimal form of coping with a personally acceptable cost to benefit ratio. The present theme allows participants to review the interplay between substance use and various existential issues and to recognize substance use as a legitimate attempt at solving the challenges of existence. Make no mistake: the point of the theme is not to endorse substance use but to recognize its partial rationality as a coping strategy. Helping clients see substance use as a creative, albeit problematic, form of existential coping, allows them to regain the belief in themselves as rational creatures and to move away from a self-critical, demoralizing, depressogenic view of themselves.

The following is a sample of questions that can be used to provide the overview of the interplay between substance use and search for meaning:

How does substance use help you feel free?

How does substance use help you understand who/what you are?

How does substance use help you deal with lack of meaning?

How does substance use help you feel connected with others?

How does substance use help you transcend the routine and the meaninglessness of life?

How does substance use help you deal with confusion, ambiguity, and complexity of life?

How does substance use help you deal with pain and suffering of adversity?

How does substance use help you deal with your mortality, death and non-being?

Theme 8 – Meaning of Transition

The final topic addresses the meaning of transition, the existential challenge of closure, the existentiality of ambiguity.

The Search Continues, Dealing with Ambiguity.

The theme begins with a review of clients' "journey" in the group. More specifically, facilitators encourage clients to review what, if anything, they have learned and understood about themselves, what, if anything, has changed about them. As clients are helped to tally up the tentative answers in their search for meaning, they are also encouraged to take an inventory of the questions that remain to be answered. Facilitators may further ask: "Where do you go from here?" While mostly rhetorical, this question acknowledges the unavoidable, inevitable ambiguity of the continuing search for meaning and of life as a journey. Facilitators may invite clients to process what this ambiguity "feels like."

Dealing with Transition and Closure.

Closure, termination, parting, ending, and separation are unique existential moments. Substance use clients are invited to explore the meaning of such transitions and are helped to recognize that such transitions present opportunities for existential meaning. The facilitators are likely to encounter references to past abandonment, lack of closure, resulting sadness and loneliness, and personal vows to never open up and get emotionally close to anyone. To help clients find solace in meaning-focused suffering, facilitators may use such questions as: "From the existential standpoint, what can we learn/gain from things coming to an end? What existential sense can we make of the sadness we experience when something ends? From the existential standpoint, what opportunities do departures offer? What beginnings do endings offer? If you follow on this path to recovery, what you are leaving behind and what are you moving towards?"

Evaluation of the Meaning of Life Group Protocol

The Meaning of Life group, as noted above, was initially designed as a part of a comprehensive substance use treatment curriculum and was subsequently applied in the context of a residential correctional substance use treatment program that took place in a program devoted pod=cellblock of a county jail in Pittsburgh, Pennsylvania.

No quantitative evaluation of the Meaning of Life group modality has yet been undertaken. In the author's direct clinical experience of administering the Meaning of Life group, the group appeared to be one of the favorite group modalities of the overall treatment curriculum and appeared to serve as a potent cohesion-building clinical event for any given cohort of admitted clients that underwent the Meaning of Life group early on in their participation in the treatment program. The following are a sample of client statements about the Meaning of Life group; these statements are taken from a weekly newsletter ("The Weekly Fix") issued by the inmates that participated in the program in question.

Inmate client M. H. (The Weekly Fix, Issue 10), poses the question to himself: "What is the meaning of my life?" and proceeds to recap the existential vector of his life of "getting closer to the dope man." M. H. concludes: "Today I was going over my notes and realized that there is a lot of meaning to my life. I am thankful for different options in recovery. I don't have to become a slave to anything again, in fact, I realize I never did. I have choices, that's where I am at!" This client's writing exemplifies a kind of existential life-review that serves as a useful platform of cognitive dissonance that eventually ferments into a motivation to change. Note this client's retrospective embracing of responsibility and an encouraging awareness of remaining opportunities for meaning.

Inmate H. T. (The Weekly Fix, Issue 12) philosophizes in response to the Meaning of Life group: "How deep does it need to be when what we've read is being written by us? How far do we need to go when walking to where we are already? How can we lose contact with reality, when it's all real?"

Inmate J. B. (The Weekly Fix, Issue 33) writes in response to the star-gazing=navigational metaphor from the Meaning of Life group (see session 1 details above): "Much of what you will face in your life is currently hidden from your view. No mirrors, windshields or navigational devices will let you see everything that awaits you ahead. When in doubt, look up, when troubled, look within, and when in darkness, always follow the Star." This particular elaboration of the star-gazing metaphor from the Meaning of Life group illustrates the emerging internalization of the treatment message of meaning as a "navigational" tool.

Inmate J. F. (The Weekly Fix, Issue 33): "Today life emerges from within and does not derive from the people around me. So it's important to find human guidance within myself or desperately search for

identity.'' This sentiment parallels some of the ideas that tend to be
verbalized in response to the Meaning of Life sub-theme of the ''meaning of self'' that inevitably results in the discussion of the cost-to-
benefit ratio of the search for external validation and definitions of self
predicated on others' expectations versus an independent approval
and definition of self.

The same inmate, J. F., writes in the Weekly Fix Issue 31: ''When
(the facilitator) started asking me what would I do if I only had a
certain time frame to live, that started making me really think and put
things in perspective. Since death is the end of all possibilities, a man's
merit lies in his knowledge.'' J. F. continues with sharing his ideas on
what is meaningful to him and concludes: ''True worth is to know the
meaning of life to me.'' Note the apparent safety of the Meaning of
Life forum that allowed this inmate client to express an often unpopular
for substance use setting atheistic view of death as ''the end of all
possibilities'' and the poignant redefining of the meaning of life as
knowing the meaning of life. This level of philosophical and existential
seeking is not unusual, in my experience, and presents an invaluable
clinical asset for leveraging motivation for change.

Inmate W. S. (The Weekly Fix, Issue 21) writes: ''Recovery equals
change, and change means doing things differently. The problem
has been that most of times I resisted doing things differently, what
I've been doing was not working. But at least I was familiar with it.
It took courage to step into the unknown.'' This sentiment parallels

the Meaning of Life group normalizing discussions of the feelings associated with the meaning of transitions as well as the meaning of meaninglessness and the substance use as a form of coping with the challenge of change.

Inmate client T. G. (The Weekly Fix, Issue 28) mentions: "By the time I came to (the program) my heart was set on not using, but I still wavered about doing crime. Through the Meaning of Life, reading my Bible, and the Crime and Recovery classes, my motivation not to do crime is much stronger today." This statement likely echoes the Meaning of Life discussions about the "meaning of self" in which correctional substance use clients have an opportunity to own the fact that we are, at least, in part, what we do. For many substance use clients for whom crime was purely instrumental as a way of obtaining the means to purchase drugs, the "meaning of self" discussion allows them to bring the meaning of their criminality into a dissonant focus with what they like to think of themselves. This is further separately addressed in the Crime and Recovery group protocol that is part of the Recovery Equation treatment curriculum (Somov & Somova, 2003).

Inmate T. A. (The Weekly Fix, Issue 23) writes about time, a frequent side topic to emerge from the Meaning of Life group sessions: "The older I get, the shorter my life seems. Short as life is, I make it shorter by the careless waste of time I spend each day getting high." This inmate further lays out the case of re-claiming the time that is yet to be lost and captures this point in an effectively paradoxical title of his article, "From Death to Life," reversing the typical intuitive sequence one would expect, equating his "using" life with meaningless mindlessness.

Another inmate client, O. W. (The Weekly Fix, Issue 9), in an article entitled "Time" alludes to one of the Meaning of Life group questions: "Is time doing you? Or are you doing time? Great questions for sure." This client explores the double pun of doing correctional time and also doing time as an active recovery stance as a way of preventing a waste of time and a waste of life. This sense of temporal urgency was observed to be a frequent by-product of the Meaning of Life group discussions and appeared to function as a marker of the emerging existential awakening.

Conclusion

Logotherapy is a uniquely valuable pre-rehabilitation and post-rehabilitation substance use treatment modality. As a pre-rehabilitation clinical tool, logotherapy, as an existential analysis of one's values and attitudes that is "particularly concerned with making men conscious of their responsibility" (Fabry, 1955, p. 29), serves to complement the process of motivational enhancement for a client embarking on the path of recovery. As a post-rehabilitation clinical tool, logotherapy is "prophylactic in preventing a relapse" (Lukas, 1979, p. 264). Indeed, as noted above, there is more to life than recovery. Recovery, just like substance use, is but a means to an end, not an end in and of itself. The proposed Meaning of Life group treatment protocol offers substance use clients a systematic approach to examining the purpose of their recovery.

References

Crumbaugh, J.C. (1979). Logotherapy: new help for problem drinkers. Burnham Inc.

Fabry, J. (1988). Guideposts to meaning: discovering what really matters. Oakland, CA: New Harbinger Publications, Inc.

Fabry, J. B., Bulka, R. P. & Sahakian, W. S. (Eds.), (1979). Logotherapy in Action. New York: Jason Aronson.

Folkman, S. (1984). Personal control and stress and coping processes: A theoretical analysis. Journal of Personality and Social Psychology, 46, 839-852.

Frankl, V. (1955). The doctor and the soul: from psychotherapy to logotherapy. New York: Alfred A. Knopf.

Frankl, V. (1978). The unheard cry for meaning: psychotherapy and humanism. New York: Simon & Schuster.

Jellinek, E. M. (1972). The disease concept of alcoholism. New Haven, CT: College and University Press.

Linville, P.W. (1985). Self-complexity and affective extremity: don't put all your eggs in one cognitive basket. Social Cognition, 3, 94-120.

Lukas, E. (1979). A supplemental form of therapy for addicts. In J. B. Fabry, R. P. Bulka & W. S. Sahakian (Eds.), Logotherapy in action. New York: Jason Aronson.

Peele, S. (1999). Diseasing of America: how we allowed recovery zealots and the treatment industry to convince us we're out of control. Jossey-Bass.

Saunders, B., Wilkinson, C., & Allsop, S. (1991). Motivational intervention with heroin users attending a methadone clinic. In W. R.Miller & S. Rollnick (Eds)., Motivational interviewing: preparing people to change addictive behavior. (pp.279 – 292). New York: Guilford Press.

Somov, P.G. & Somova, M. J. (2003), Recovery Equation: Motivational Enhancement/Choice Awareness/Use Prevention: an Innovative Clinical Curriculum for Substance Use Treatment. Imprint Books, ISBN: 1594571929.

Psychodrama & Substance Use Treatment

Somov, P. G. (2008). A Psychodrama Group for Substance Use Relapse Prevention Training. The Arts in Psychotherapy, 38, 151-161.

Abstract

The article reviews utilization of psychodrama group therapy in the context of drug and alcohol treatment and introduces a specific application of psychodrama group therapy for the purposes of relapse prevention. The proposed psychodrama group format features facilitator guidelines for directing relapse prevention behavioral role plays, substance-use specific role plays, and a format for post-role-play processing of group participants' experiences.

Psychodrama is Group Therapy

Psychodrama is an action method pioneered by Moreno, one of the founders of group psychotherapy (Corsini, 1955). A therapeutic modality in which "people enact scenes from their lives, dreams or fantasies in an effort to express unexpressed feelings, gain new insights and understandings, and practice new and more satisfying behaviors" (Garcia & Buchanan, 2000, p. 162), psychodrama would appear uniquely positioned to allow individuals in substance use treatment to practice relapse prevention skills. And yet psychodrama, as a clinical modality, appears to be underutilized by the mainstay of substance use group work. For example, Brook and Spitz, in their otherwise comprehensive review of group modalities in the field of substance use treatment, "The Group Therapy of Substance Abuse" (2002), did not include a description of psychodrama. Their book makes a few "one-word mentions" of psychodrama in passing and devotes only one free-standing paragraph on the history of psychodrama with substance use population tucked away at the end of the book. Robert Landy, professor and director of the Drama Therapy Program at New York University, in his 1997 pre-millennium status report article entitled "Drama Therapy – The state of the Art," enumerates at least sixteen specific client populations but fails to mention the population of substance use. Similarly, Frances, Miller & Mack, in their authoritative and much anticipated 2005 "Clinical Textbook of Addictive Disorders, Third Edition" fail to mention psychodrama. Coombs and Howatt, the authors of "The Addiction Counselor's Desk Reference" (2005), a truly panoramic resource, offer only a two-line definition of psychodrama in the back-matter of the four hundred plus pages book. Their definition of psychodrama as "adjunct to psychotherapy in which the patient acts out certain roles and incidents" (p. 373) offers a clue to the short shrift given to psychodrama in the substance use literature: despite a rather substantial history of the use of psychodrama with the substance use population, psychodrama is still viewed as an "adjunct to psychotherapy" for substance use, not as a bona fide group treatment modality.

One possible explanation for the underutilization of psychodrama in the group-work driven drug and alcohol rehabilitation field might be a failure to appreciate that psychodrama is, unambiguously, a form of group therapy. Another possible explanation is that while some attempts have been made to extend the practice of psychodrama to the field of addiction treatment, the psychodrama literature has largely failed to crystallize a psychodrama application that is specific to the goals of relapse prevention. Furthermore, psychodrama has historically relied on psychoanalytic and interpersonal frame of reference which places psychodrama, as a clinical modality, somewhat at odds with the fact that most of the present drug and alcohol treatment, in general, and relapse prevention training, specifically, in the U.S. appears to be informed by the cognitive-behavioral paradigm. Avrahami's 2003 article on the interplay between CBT and psychodrama is an encouraging but largely isolated attempt to formally shift the vector of psychodrama practice and psychodrama literature towards the cognitive-behavioral orientation. Finally, psychodrama in its classic form, both in its conceptual postulate of spontaneity and creativity as well as in its theatrical and improvisational logistics, does not quite fit in with the outcome-oriented rehabilitation culture that emphasizes canned protocols.

The present article proposes a psychodrama application that is specifically designed for the purposes of substance use relapse prevention training, that has been adapted to the cognitive-behavioral frame of reference, and that offers the director (group facilitator) more ways to direct and manage the outcome of what happens on the psychodramatic group stage. The proposed modality, originally described in Somov & Somova (2003) and piloted in a residential correctional drug and alcohol treatment program in an American county jail, represents a psychodramatic treatment modality that can be used as a relapse prevention skill-practice group as part of the overall relapse prevention training curriculum or as a stand-alone relapse prevention group modality.

An Incomplete Evolution of Psychodrama in Addiction Treatment

Since Moreno conducted the first psychodrama session on April 1st, 1921 in his Vienna Theatre of Spontaneity and throughout the 20th century, psychodrama evolved from a kind of broad-band psychoanalytic action method (in which "audiences suggested topics" and "the troupe" of professional actors "enacted them to explore and resolve the underlying social issues") to a set of progressively population-specific "practical applications for everyday use" (Garcia & Buchanan, 2000, p.

162). The evolution of psychodrama, however, appears to be somewhat incomplete. In theory, the unique clinical promise of psychodrama is that it is both analytical (awareness-building) and behavioral
(behavior-modifying) as it offers a "significant advantage in changing
behavior both through exploratory, healing role play and through role
training or practicing more functional behaviors" (Dayton, 2003, p.
179). While Rustin and Olsson (1993, p. 12) note that "psychodrama
has been widely used in the treatment of addiction patients" and that
Moreno himself "treated alcoholics in psychodrama," the applications
of psychodrama in addictions treatment has remained primarily analytical and focused on "exploratory, healing role play" to foster insight into
one's inter- and intra-personal addiction dynamics rather than focusing
on "role training or practicing" relapse prevention behaviors and skills
to directly effectuate behavior- and habit-modification.

An example of such incomplete evolution can be found in
Woodward's "Acting for Change: the evolution of a psychodrama
group" (2004). Woodward describes Acting for Change, a psychodrama group that was offered from 1994 through 2001 at ACCEPT, a
London agency that started out as an alternative to (if not a refuge
from) AA and provided abstinence-based day programs and a therapeutic community for individuals with problematic alcohol use. Woodward (2004) offers a description of an evolution of a psychodrama
group for alcohol abusers as a function of the evolution of the agency'
treatment philosophy that changed from an approach that originally
focused on "insight and underlying issues" of alcohol abuse to an
approach that focused on "self-management, negotiation of boundaries,

and containment" (p. 133). Woodward notes that the original Acting for Change psychodrama for alcohol abusers was psychoanalytically-informed and "often concentrated on childhood issues and the development of insight leading to a catharsis" (p. 137). As the agency's treatment philosophy evolved away from the psychoanalytic perspective towards a "more contemporary psychodynamic model" (p. 133), which also introduced "didactic and cognitive elements" offered "in the informative sessions such as the alcohol and therapy seminar, the self-management group, and relapse prevention" (p. 140), the new Acting for Change psychodrama for alcohol abusers appears to have remained largely insight-oriented and awareness-building rather behavior- and habit-modifying in its scope. And indeed, as the agency's treatment philosophy shifted from psychoanalytic, insight-oriented frame of reference towards at least partial focus on skills of self-regulation and relapse prevention, the new Acting for Change psychodrama still remained insight-oriented in its vector. Woodward writes that in "rethinking the delivery" of this psychodrama for alcohol abusers he felt that the "real value was the externalization of internal issues through enactment" (p. 142). This new and reformed psychodrama included such enactments as having clients "talk to the 'bottle' and reverse roles with it briefly" and "externalization of internal splits" designed to raise "personal awareness of ambivalence" (p. 143). Aside from this awareness-building role play, the new psychodrama did include role training which involved "brainstorming past and current roles" and giving clients an opportunity to "think of a role they would like to be in, then speak from that role" (p. 144). While this kind of brainstorming of roles suggests a significant evolution from the "old school" emphasis on spontaneous enactments that reveal the unconscious by way of transference to a "new school" approach of consciously thinking through the parameters of a desired role, Woodward's description of this role training does not, however, suggest that this role training evolved far enough to include specific practice of recovery oriented interpersonal stances or behavioral rehearsal of relapse prevention skills.

The "Sobriety Shop," a psychodrama exercise for use with the substance use population pioneered "in the early 1950s" by Hannah Weiner, a student of Moreno's (Rustin & Olsson, 1993, p. 12), is another example of an analytically- rather than behaviorally-oriented application of psychodrama to the problems of substance use. While Rustin and Olsson note that the exercise "helps patients learn new behaviors needed for maintaining abstinence and anticipate the problems patients will face in their recovery," this psychodrama exercise "in which personal qualities that have contributed to the patient's addictive illness are exchanged for desirable qualities that will help the patients stay sober," (1993, p. 12), to my analysis, is primarily insight-oriented. Despite the behavior-modifying mandate of the exercise, the "Sobriety Shop" remains more of an exploration and an assessment than a behavior-modification training. Rustin and Olsson in the conclusion of their paper summarize the benefits of the "Sobriety Shop:" the exercise "offers an opportunity for several patients to explore their issues in a single session;" the exercise "allows for wider group participation;" allows patients to "enjoy the spontaneity and playfulness" and to "drop their defenses, which permits them to deal more authentically with their issues;" and from the facilitator's perspective, the exercise "provides an avenue for participation evaluation" (1993, p. 21).

Dayton (2003), in writing on the application of psychodrama in the treatment of addiction and trauma in women, speaks clearly about the role training value of psychodrama: "We learn through experience. Psychodrama can provide an arena where anticipated, desired, needed, or feared roles can be explored and new behaviors 'tried on for size.' One of psychodrama's important uses is to provide practice in under-developed roles so that the anxiety and newness of a role can be explored and worked through in a clinical environment" (p. 193).

Dayton, like Woodward and other psychodrama clinicians that operate in the addictions context, appears to be unambiguously clear about the value of practicing recovery behaviors. And yet, despite this clearly behavioral mandate of skill practice, the actual practice of psychodrama in the field of addiction appears to be conspicuously void of any substantive emphasis on relapse prevention. A case in point is Dayton's (2003) set of three goals designed to leverage the role training benefits of psychodrama in treating addicted female trauma clients; these goals are: "to provide practice and training in adapting to a new role," "to explore the nuances of a role as it relates to the self," and "to explore the impact of the role from the position of the other" (p. 193). The goal that is conspicuously absent from this addiction-oriented application of psychodrama is "to practice a substance use recovery oriented role and relapse prevention skills."

Psychodrama for addictions has, indeed, evolved from its historically exploratory, diagnostic unraveling of the unconscious dynamics behind substance use to motivation-leveraging and ambivalence-clarifying dialogues with the "bottle" and up to a threshold of change at which substance use clients "try on for size" a recovery role. This is an incomplete evolution: the above examples of psychodrama for addiction highlight the fact that psychodrama remains underutilized as an excellent behavioral supplement to relapse prevention training. Despite its two-fold benefit of exploratory role play and role training, all too often, the former takes precedence over the latter. Psychodrama, in its original mandate, is both analytical (awareness-building) and behavioral (habit/role/behavior-modifying). Consequently, it would appear that as long as psychodrama for addictions continues to be primarily focused on exploratory, awareness-building role play to the exclusion of behavior-modifying role training of such specific recovery skills as relapse prevention, the evolution of psychodrama for the treatment of addictions is incomplete.

Dysfunctional Spontaneity of Relapse Prevention

In trying to make sense of the resistance of the psychodrama movement to prescriptive role rehearsal of specific relapse prevention behaviors, it helps to examine Moreno's canon of spontaneity and creativity. Moreno (2000) postulated that the spontaneous and creative have the survival advantage and that "all dysfunction is caused by a lack of spontaneity and/or creativity" (p. 172). This spontaneity dysfunction

can manifest as either paralysis of spontaneity (becoming "frozen and
unable to act" when faced with a novel situation), or impulsivity
("action without reflection"), or reactivity ("reflection without a here
and now action," i.e. a re-enactment of an old action that might have
been appropriate for a situation in the past but might not be an appropriate response to the current situation) (p. 172). Moreno's emphasis
on spontaneity and creativity shaped the vector of psychodrama development: from the days of the Vienna-based Theatre of Spontaneity to
the present, psychodrama emphasizes being in the moment, "living in
complete harmony and unity while staying connected to the social
realities of the here and now" (Garcia & Buchanan, 2000, p. 172), in a
state of here-and-now mindfulness and absorption, in a state of "flow"
(Csikszentmihalyi, 1991) characterized by peak spontaneity and
disappearance of ego. In short, psychodrama emphasizes here-and-now
action and, in its classic form, resists rehearsal which is a prescriptive
re-action/re-enactment of a previously agreed upon role. In this,
Morenean psychodramatic theatre of spontaneity stops being theatre
per se since theatre, in its classic form, is nothing other than a re-
enactment of an internalized role, the word that "draws its origin from
the Latin rotulus, which is the name of the roll of paper or vellum upon
which the actor's part was written" (Pittruzzella, 2004, p. 92). Pittruzzella clarifies the function of a role: "role makes us think, therefore,
of a prescribed sequence of behavior – words, gestures, expressions,
bodily attitudes and other communication signs – coherent with a
definition of the character moving within given circumstances" (p. 92).
While this kind of role training would be ideal for a relapse prevention

application of psychodrama in which a client protagonist could be exposed to hypothetical recovery-challenging circumstances in order to practice a "prescribed sequence" of relapse prevention behaviors, such re-enactment of a recovery role would appear incongruent with the Morenean emphasis on real time spontaneity. The result, unfortunately, is the kind of psychodrama application to addiction that results in dysfunctional spontaneity of relapse prevention. Substance use clients that participate in psychodrama applications for addiction, even when confined to the "framework of a vignette" that involves a possible recovery-specific scene (Woodward, 2004, p. 143), are essentially left to improvise their way through a relapse prevention response.

Whereas the theatre-of-spontaneity approach to psychodrama applications for addiction may be invaluable in terms of its diagnostic, awareness-building value, the use of psychodrama for relapse prevention cannot afford improvisation. To be exact, the improvisation of relapse prevention has to be re-calibrated to the spontaneity and creativity of the application of a prescribed relapse prevention cluster of behaviors and interpersonal stances, not to the spontaneity and creativity of the character per se. The distinction between the improvisation of the recovery character and the improvisation of how this recovery character acts when presented with various scenes of life is a paramount one. For psychodrama to remain psychodrama and not be reduced to an oversimplified behavioral role-play, the protagonists do have to practice spontaneity and creativity of the behavior; however, if psychodrama applications for addiction are to offer more than exploratory role training of the recovery persona, psychodrama has to offer clients a prescribed recovery role that, among other things, includes a specific relapse prevention algorithm, with an encouragement that the protagonist practice the spontaneity of application of the recovery behaviors while remaining in character (of recovery). In short, for good performance, an actor has to have a method and to apply it with spontaneity.

Relapse Prevention Psychodrama

Relapse prevention psychodrama, proposed here, was piloted by the author in the context of a residential non-medical drug and alcohol correctional treatment program housed in a county jail. The Lapse/Relapse Prevention Group, as it was listed on the program's clinical curriculum, was, in fact, a culmination of an overall prevention skill-power training module that began with a didactic introduction of the distinctions between Slip, Lapse and Relapse, and, then, proceeded with a systematic introduction of four separate prevention plans, namely, those of Slip Prevention, Lapse Prevention, Relapse Prevention and Relapse Termination plans (Somov & Somova, 2003). Following the initial didactic introduction of Slip Prevention, Slip Prevention was practiced in the context of a peer-led Slip Prevention Self-Help Circle. This peer-led Slip Prevention group ran parallel to the introductory Prevention Skill-Power Training Group. When the Prevention Skill-Power Training Group concluded with the presentation of all four use prevention and use termination plans, the correctional substance use clients "graduated" to Lapse/Relapse Prevention Practice Group, which constituted use prevention oriented psychodrama (to be referred to henceforward as LP/RP Psychodrama).

Rationale

The rationale behind the LP/RP Psychodrama is three-fold. First, this addiction-specific psychodrama group allows clients to practice their use prevention and use termination plans through a variety of role-plays and recovery vignettes. This psychodrama also group allows clinicians to engage in direct observation of clients' prevention skills and to provide clients with constructive/corrective feedback. Finally, the LP/RP psychodrama group enhances clients' sense of membership in a kind of recovery-oriented "social atom"(a network of recovery-significant relationships) with the hope of enhancing clients' overall treatment compliance and aims to increase the possibility of exporting the program-established recovery network to clients' post-discharge/post-release lives.

The Instruments and the Process of LP/RP Psychodrama

Moreno (2000) elaborated the following five instruments of psycho-drama: the stage (setting), the director (the therapist), the protagonist (the client in treatment who is the focus of the given psychodramatic enactment), the auxiliary egos (the supporting actors that reveal various aspects of the protagonist's phenomenology), and the audience (the group). Furthermore, psychodrama offers several distinct processes:

the so-called warm-up, the casting (the selection of the protagonist and auxiliaries), the action, and the post-action processing or sharing. The following is a review of these items of format as they apply to the LP/RP Psychodrama group.

The Stage

The setting has to at least vaguely parallel the architecture of the theatre space. In practice, this is merely an issue of a boundary between stage space and audience space. Consequently, any space can be arbitrarily divided into these two realms. In the case of this particular pilot, the LP/RP Psychodrama took place in an essentially triangular room that had been previously divided in half for the purposes of a visitation room. On the author's request and with the help of the program's administration, the jail administration was gracefully willing to knock this wall down which yielded a sizeable triangle-shaped auditorium for most of the program's group activities which opened directly into the housing pod and also featured on one side a wall of windows with a view of the open air gym and, on the other side, featured a door window into a "slider" lock port that, on occasion, provided an element of random audience of the jail staff that would be awaiting passage in the "slider" from one area to another. From the psychodramatic perspective this arrangement allowed for a degree of transparency that essentially set the stage of this psychodrama on the backdrop of reality.

The Director and Director's Roles

Kellerman (1992) deconstructed the role of the psychodrama director into four roles: analyst, producer, therapist, and group leader. Woodward (2004), in his writing about a psychodrama for newly abstinent alcohol abusers, and building on the role theories of Moreno and Clayton, defined the roles of a psychodrama/group therapist as excavator, container, parent, advocate and cheerleader. Given the behavior-modifying rather than awareness-building focus of the LP/RP Psychodrama, the roles of its Director can be conceptualized as essentially two-fold: the producer and the group therapist. The LP/RP Psychodrama Director is expected to switch back and forth between these two roles depending on the specific psychodrama process. It stands to reason that during the warm-up, the Director is the group therapist in charge of leading a psychodrama group into an action phase. During the casting, the Director may intermittently assume the role of a producer or a group therapist depending on whether the dynamics of the protagonist and auxiliary ego selection require any interpersonal processing. In the action/enactment phase, the Director again alternates between the roles of a producer (should additional acting resources, for example, need to be recruited and quickly role-trained from the audience) and a group therapist (if the enactment is paused for real time feedback or processing). Finally, in the post-action phase of sharing, the Director is back to being the group therapist in charge of processing clinical material and intra-group dynamics as he or she leads the psychodrama group session to closure.

The Protagonist and the Psychodrama Group Size

The protagonist of LP/RP Psychodrama is a substance use client that
either self-selects for an enactment or is selected by the Director.
Whereas in classic psychodrama the protagonist is encouraged to be
spontaneous "rather than being an actor in a play who must follow a
script," (Garcia & Buchanan, 2000, p. 178), in lapse/relapse prevention
psychodrama the protagonist is offered a particular recovery oriented
vignette and is expected to stay in the recovery character while aiming
for a real time spontaneity and creativity of application of previously
discussed substance use prevention plans.

Feasey (2001) recommends to use closed psychodrama groups
as the "security of tenure is a must for a psychodrama group" and, in
regard to the number of participants, suggests that "psychodrama can
be very effective in groups much larger than eight" (p. 20).

In the case of the present pilot program, the LP/RP Psychodrama group consisted of approximately twenty correctional male
inmates. The drug and alcohol program in question had a typical
census of twenty five inmate clients at any given time, five of which
typically constituted new arrivals who did not participate in the LP/RP
Psychodrama until they completed a peer-led Slip Prevention Self-Help
Circle (group). While this LP/RP Psychodrama group was not technically closed, the actors' "troupe" tended to remain largely the same for
substantial periods of time and only varied with the natural turn-over of
the program participants. Given the fact that this particular LP/RP
Psychodrama group was offered in the context of a residential correc-

tional context, it was offered on a daily basis Monday through Friday for a period of several weeks. Following the run of the group, this psychodrama would be re-introduced at a later point as the composition of the program participants turned over enough for the bulk of the residents to be new admissions. As such, some of the clients that remained in the drug and alcohol program for a longer period of time would have a second opportunity at participation in the LP/RP Psycho-drama group. These second-timers would typically prove to be an invaluable resource as these "old" actor-members would be already indoctrinated to the process of psychodrama and would model the group culture for the new arrivals. Feasley (2001, p. 16) writes about the similar experience of an open psychodrama group in a hospital setting: "the group was stable, but it was a slow, open, permanent group, admitting new members as patients left. This made for a some-what different culture. Mostly it was signified by 'old' members of the group introducing new members to the culture." Unlike in Feasley's case where as a result of this open and rotating membership format there formed a "pecking order of experience and seniority, which had to be taken into account by the director" (p. 16), in the present case no such pecking order appeared evident. The "old," second-time psycho-drama participants appeared willing to come to the rescue, so to say, in the absence of volunteers for the role of a protagonist, but did not necessarily feel entitled to the psychodramatic limelight. Another advantage to having these second-timers was their willingness to publicly process their past hesitations for volunteering to be a protagonist for psychodrama, which tended to normalize the self-conscious inhibitions of the new group members.

Auxiliary Ego: The Voice of Craving

Auxiliary Ego is a psychodrama term for a supporting actor whose role is to enact an aspect of the protagonist's phenomenology. "The auxiliary ego brings life to the protagonist's world" (Garcia & Buchanan, 2000, p. 179). One of the key aspects of a substance user's phenomenology during a situation that challenges his or her commitment to recovery and may potentially result in a lapse or a relapse is an experience of a craving. Craving is often described as consisting of a combination of the behavioral impulse to use a given substance, possibly accompanied with a degree of somatic arousal, and of a cognitive element in the form of self-talk that advocates substance use at a given moment. The proposed LP/RP Prevention Psychodrama utilizes the craving aspect of a substance user's experience through the so-called Voice of Craving.

The Voice of Craving is thus a psychodramatic device that is specifically designed to allow a substance use client protagonist to externalize an aspect of his or her experience in order to practice an application of a lapse/relapse prevention plan despite the craving. The Voice of the Craving distracts, complicates, tantalizes and, as such, inoculates the protagonist to this often inevitable internal liability of a person in early substance use recovery. On a practical note, a psychodrama group member that volunteers to enact the protagonist's Voice

of Craving, in essence, narrates craving sound-bites into the protagonist's ear as those kinds of craving thoughts would be expected to
emerge as the protagonist deals with a given prevention scenario.
The Voice of Craving auxiliary ego actor is, in essence, a supporting
actor who role-plays the nagging voice of sabotage. It is recommended
that the Voice of Craving auxiliary ego actor should be physically
positioned behind the protagonist to facilitate a sense of an invisible
voice in the back of the mind. As such, the Voice of the Craving
experientially illustrates the sense of confusing overwhelm and distraction that occurs when an individual battling with lapse or relapse
prevention attempts to multi-task. The protagonists are instructed to
engage in craving control as soon as they hear the Voice of the Craving. Furthermore, the protagonists are asked to announce that they are
initiating craving control.

At the sound of this announcement by the protagonist the Voice
of the Craving supporting actor lowers down his or her voice to illustrate the fact that craving control works and the craving subsides and
eventually vanishes. The added benefit of this element is that easily-
distractible clients are, in fact, taught to utilize the method of self-
instruction by verbalizing to themselves out loud what they are about to
do in order to successfully navigate a given situational challenge to
their recovery. As the protagonist maneuvers through a role-play
scenario, the Voice of the Craving emerges at logical junctions (for
example, whenever the protagonist comes in contact with such craving
eliciting external stimuli as people, places and things, as well as whenever the protagonist might be triggered to crave by internal stimuli of

boredom, dysphoria, anger, anxiety or any other significant deviations from emotional baseline). At such points, when the Voice of the Craving becomes louder, the protagonist once again resumes craving control as necessary.

Other Auxiliary Egos in LP/RP Psychodrama: Double, Sponsor, Support Figure, Dealer, P.O.

LP/RP Psychodrama utilizes other auxiliary egos that are pertinent to the theme of substance use prevention. The Double is a stand-in auxiliary ego that represents the Protagonist. The role of a Double may be useful in several ways. For example, in a stage-within-a-stage production, the Protagonist, who is in the process of role-playing a lapse prevention vignette, might be also observing another role-play on the periphery of the clinical stage in which his or her Double is role-playing the protagonist's past handling of a similar situation in which the Protagonist ended up lapsing and/or relapsing. This allows for real-time self-reflection as well as for an experiential reference of the Protagonist's behavior that had been previously ineffective. The Double may also carefully watch the Protagonist's lapse/relapse performance and "play it back" afterwards to help the Protagonist critique his or her act. The auxiliary egos of Sponsor, Support Figure, Dealer, or P. O. (probation officer) represent the "others" from the protagonist's support and "use" networks.

Psychodrama group members that role-play the Protagonist's auxiliary egos are protagonists in their own right as well. In role-playing the Voice of the Craving, or the roles of Support Figure or the roles of a Sponsor or a Dealer or a Double, these supporting actors support their own recovery both through vicarious and direct practice of anti- and pro-recovery roles that are just as relevant for their recovery as they are for that of the Protagonist. Moreover, the practice of anti-recovery roles of the Voice of the Craving or that of a Dealer or a Drinking Buddy, the supporting actors often find themselves in motivationally leveraging states of cognitive dissonance. Furthermore, this role-play of anti-recovery roles with its resultant dissonance about one's impact on another's well-being also serves as a form of empathy-training that is of additional benefit in the correctional substance use rehabilitation setting.

The Audience: Membership in Recovery

The psychodrama audience is an interactive and validating witness to the Protagonist's stage-life. In my experience of conducting the LP/RP Psychodrama in a correctional drug and alcohol program, I came to appreciate the importance of allowing for spontaneous interaction between the acting troupe and the audience. Aside from corrective and celebratory applause and cheer-leading, the group participants in the audience often volunteered themselves as provocateurs and supporters of the Protagonist's recovery struggle in mid-play. While at times such outbursts of audience activity appeared to create an element of chaos, the participation – regardless of its vector – appeared to be of greater clinical significance than its dramatic utility. The spontaneous en-

gagement of a given audience member on either side of recovery leaked
streams of process-rich information both about his readiness for change
and the sociometry of group dynamics. More often than not, the
audience – which is typically comprised of substance clients with
varying degrees of ambivalence about going "clean" – invested their
sentiments with the protagonist, in support of his recovery. And in so
doing, the audience would inadvertently unite around the common
denominator of change and recovery, thus becoming a kind of unoffi-
cial pro-recovery microcosm, ready to be internalized both by the
protagonist and the audience members themselves.

LP/RP Psychodrama Process: The Warm-Up

As noted above, the psychodrama offers several distinct processes: the
warm-up, the casting, the action, and the sharing. Psychodrama action
begins with the warm-up. Garcia & Buchanan (2000) note that "the
warm-up is the time when group members begin focusing on the issues
that they may wish to explore during the session." The specific nature
of warm-up and its extent vary by the setting. Psychodrama conducted
on an outpatient setting, in a psychodrama group without a specific
population focus, would appear to require more extensive and more
exploratory warm-up than a psychodrama group that meets several
times a week in a problem-specific rehabilitation setting. Woodward
(2004), in writing about a psychodrama application for substance users,
writes that clients in a therapeutic community are "likely to be
'warmed-up' to ongoing issues most of the time" (p. 142). This was

certainly the case in the example of this LP/RP Psychodrama group. Consequently, the warm-up typically involved a brief discussion of a client's "hypotheticals" (in which clients are instructed to problem-solve hypothetical prevention opportunities on their own, as home-work) or a discussion of clients' "prevention memos" (in which clients are asked to audio-tape revelations about their craving triggers from their participation in the Slip Prevention Self-Help Circle, as well as the audio versions of their LP, RP and RT plans) (Somov & Somova, 2003). Thus, the 5-10 minute warm-up would usually involve hearing out a couple of client reports about how they had handled a "hypotheti-cal" challenge to their recovery and/or listening to a play-back of someone's "prevention memo" cassette.

LP/RP Psychodrama Action: 20 Recovery Vignettes

LP/RP Psychodrama action would begin with casting: the Director would call for volunteers. The Director would typically avoid casting anyone by appointment and reduce his or her authority in selection only to an occasional suggestion to a given group member about trying this or that role. In the rare event that no one volunteered, the Director would proceed to process the meaning of this non-participation until motivation for participation would be re-leveraged or until the end of the psychodrama session. Following the casting, the Director would "walk and talk" with the respective members of the cast to set up a recovery oriented vignette that would at a minimum provide an oppor-tunity for practice of lapse prevention (LP) but could also be easily converted to an opportunity for relapse prevention (RP). The following is a sample of twenty-one such recovery vignettes to role-play in substance use prevention oriented psychodrama. The vignettes below, in part, reflect the correctional nature of the rehabilitation context in which this LP/RP Psychodrama was piloted. Clinicians are naturally advised to tailor the LP/RP vignettes to the specifics of their target populations.

"Sponsor Gone Bad"

Client discovered that his sponsor has lapsed or relapsed. Alternatively, a client who is struggling with a lapse or relapse prevention task invites his or her sponsor on the scene and the latter develops a craving of their own.

"Found a Stash"

Client is instructed to role play a LP after he or she finds a stash of cash and/or drugs from the previous run.

"To Sell or Not to Sell"

Client has been unsuccessful in trying to get a job and has been approached with an offer of selling drugs. Alternatively, the client has been doing well for some time but lacks money to send the family on a trip to Disneyland. Consequently, he ponders "flipping one or two Gs" from his savings to fill up the deficit in his budget.

"Street Come-on"

Client is instructed to role play a bread-and-butter classic of being offered drugs on the street. He might be waiting for a bus, or coming back from work, or just sitting in a park.

"Meeting Got to Me"

Client, after a self-help meeting, has heard too much about other people's bottoms and is pondering a peek into his own abyss.

"Pay Day"

Client came into some cash and/or has been asked to go to a bar or to celebrate the end of the work week with his or her work buddies.

"Downsizing"

Client has been fired with or without severance pay. Severance pay essentially synthesizes the Pay Day scenario with the Got Fired scenario.

"Communication Break-Down"

As the client enacts his role-play, the facilitator suddenly signals to him that the client cannot access his support for one of the following reasons: he forgot the phone number; he does not have a cell phone or change to use pay phone; the support person is not answering or is not emotionally available; the support person answers the call, asks to call back, but does not call back.

"Disabled Enabler"

The client is offered a situation of pseudo-support in which his or her "support" person enables substance use.

"Back on the Set"

Client is instructed to role play a LP after he found himself back on the "set" (in his/her substance use environment, i.e. back in the "old company" of using friends, or back in the neighborhood, etc.).

"Using Peer"

Client has been offered drugs by a halfway house roommate or a self-help meeting peer or a fellow participant in the substance use treatment program.

"Walking off the Paper"

Client is instructed to role play a LP after he has completed the conditions of his parole or probation or after release from the correctional setting. In short, the client has met his legal obligations and entertained the idea of celebrating.

"Drugs and Sex"

Client is instructed to role play a LP which involves any number of situations in which clients' partners are either current or former users. Alternatively, client is triggered to use in the course of or after a sexual encounter due to his or her past combination of using and intimacy.

"Righteous Child"

Client is instructed to role play a LP which involves an altercation with his or her adolescent child who is either caught using or selling and righteously excuses his or her behavior by blaming the parent for modeling the very behavior in question.

"Giving a Lift"

Client is instructed to role play a LP after he or she, in good faith, gives a ride to a fellow person in recovery to a self-help meeting; as the passenger exits the client's car, the driver discovers that his passenger inadvertently dropped a vile of crack or a stamp bag. Alternatively, the passenger offers client, the driver, drugs "for old time's sake," or as a form of repayment.

"Family Function"

Client is instructed to role play a LP after he is offered alcohol and/or drugs in the course of a family function (reunion, birthday, holiday, wedding, etc.).

"Relationship Trouble"

Client experiences a loss of relationship (break-up, quarrel, separation, divorce).

"Home-Coming"

Client discovers that his or her partner had been unfaithful while client had been in a residential treatment facility.

"Devise Your Own Role-Play"

Clients are invited to role-play a vignette of their own. They are asked to ponder the types of situations they are likely to encounter upon completion of treatment, or while in treatment, and to role-play the corresponding scenarios.

"Change the Future by Changing the Past"

In this psychodrama clients are offered an opportunity to think of a pivotal moment in their recent history that resulted in their current circumstance or in the break-down of their recovery. They are offered to re-do what had happened, to enact a chain of events that would have allowed them to prevent the chain of events that resulted in their current predicament. This role-play typically, but not always, involves a re-enactment of the antecedents of the situation in question without substance use.

The guidelines for the behavioral role-plays involve an emphasis on acting in real time. If, for example, enacting the specific steps of their lapse or relapse prevention plans, clients are encouraged to do so in real time and not compress these personalized use prevention protocols in time. For example, clients are encouraged to do their craving control in real time (i.e. to actually take six to twelve deep abdominal breaths and to actually take time to use their previously established craving control self-talk) (Somov & Somova, 2003). The guidelines for protagonists involve permission to create "obstacles" and to "throw in curve balls." The supporting actors agree to respond to real-time instructions from the Director (usually non-verbal signals). This is used in the situation in which a given Protagonist appears to be easily distraught or con-fused. For example, when the Protagonist enacts calling a support figure on the phone, the facilitator may signal to the auxiliary ego that role-plays a Dealer or Using Peer to "pull back" for a time being.

Alternatively, if the Protagonist appears to be "on the ball," the Director may nonverbally or inconspicuously signal a supporting actor to create an additional obstacle for the Protagonist. For example, if a Protagonist role-plays calling a Sponsor for support, the Director may signal to the Sponsor to not answer the phone or to act like a "sponsor that went bad." This technique of Curve Balls parallels the complexity of life and as such has the value of generalization and realism. The strategy of creating obstacles is in contrast with often naïve expectations that substance use clients in recovery have about the ease of access to, utility and dependability of their support network. In directing LP/RP role-plays it is important to let the primary actor experience at least some frustration as a process of inoculation against future stress. Both didactically and through group process (in the sharing phase), the Director in his/her Group Therapist role emphasizes that the presence of lapse/relapse prevention plans is not an automatic assurance of stress-free recovery. The group leader aims to harness Protagonists' frustration from these "curve balls" as motivational leverage to increase clients' commitment to the practice of recovery skills. It should be noted that the LP/RP Psychodrama in question is informed by an approach to recovery that emphasizes self-sufficiency of use prevention skill-power (Somov & Somova, 2003).

The value of this obstacle strategy, however, has to be balanced against the therapeutic goal of enhancing clients' self-efficacy. With this in mind, another guideline for LP/RP Psychodrama is the principle of "Always a Happy End." What this means is that a given psychodrama is not complete until the Protagonist demonstrates a successful resolution of the prevention challenge in hand. This may involve having the Protagonist pause, process the lessons of the experience, and redo the role-plays until the recovery objectives are met. In some cases, this principle meant that the particular psychodrama would last more than one session.

LP/RP Psychodrama Sharing: Processing Group Dynamics & Lessons of Prevention

Sharing is the concluding phase of the psychodrama process. In its classic form it involves the processing of group participants' personal experiences. Feasey (2001) suggests that the Directors give the protagonists an opportunity to process the material on their own immediately following the enactment. Feasey (2001) recommends that the Director first attend to the auxiliaries. In Lapse/Relapse Prevention psychodrama the group leader would explore the "lessons of prevention," triggered memories or feelings, revelations and epiphanies of the supporting actors as well as the audience. Questions along the lines of "In what way was this about you?" help engage the audience in sharing ways in which they identified with the action on stage.

Feasey (2001, p.74), in writing about the closure in sharing, also speaks of the importance of "de-roling" in which the protagonist, for example, in exiting the stage and returning to the circle of the group, i.e. in "moving from one reality to another," would "de-role," for example, a prop of a paperback book from its role as a diary back to being but a paperback. Similarly, Feasey (2001) feels it is necessary to

have the auxiliaries to formally "de-role:" If, for example, a psychodrama group member named Fred role-played John, then Fred needs to
say that he is Fred, not John. Lipman (2003) also acknowledges the
importance of "de-roling" as a means of shedding "immediate sociometric links to the protagonist's world" (p. 12) but proposes a less
formal method for "de-roling" through merely processing how auxiliaries' roles pertained to their own experience.

Lipman (2003) notes that following a psychodramatic enactment there might be shifts in the sociometry of the group. While some
psychodrama theorists object to the use of post-action sharing for
discussion of such sociometric shifts in group dynamics, the majority
of psychodrama authors appear to be in consensus on the utility of this
kind of interpersonal processing. In my experience, exploring the
sociometric/group-dynamic valence of such psychodrama events as the
frequency (or lack thereof) of the self-selection into the role of protagonist, protagonist's choices of auxiliaries, the audience's response to
a specific psychodrama (that might be at times more reflective of the
interpersonal dynamics between the audience members and the specific
individuals on stage than of the actual clinical value of the performance) is clinically valuable, particularly for understanding group
dynamics of a cohort-driven rehabilitation treatment in which clients
are grouped on the basis of the timing of their admission to the program. In my experience, I have also observed that "de-roling" of both
protagonists and auxiliaries helps actors process any interpersonal
sentiments towards each other elicited by the enactment. This is
particularly valuable in lapse/relapse psychodramatic enactments in

which auxiliaries that enact the anti-recovery roles (of Voice of the Craving, Dealer, Using Peer, etc.) improvise additional obstacles or "curve balls" for the protagonist as part of challenging the protagonist's spontaneity of application of use prevention know-how.

In "de-roling" the Protagonist, I have found it helpful to follow a particular sequence of questions that allows the Protagonist to first focus on the what he or she had appreciated about his/her performance, followed by questions to the Audience and the Auxiliaries about what they had appreciated or liked about the Protagonist's performance. Having elicited positive feedback, the Director opens the door into constructive feedback: "What in your opinion could have been improved upon?" I find that having a standard format to the processing of the role-play puts clients at ease and gives them a sense of control over how the feedback will be given.

Conclusion

Psychodrama, as a clinically rich group therapy modality, has been underutilized in the substance use/addictions treatment setting. The present article explored a particular application of psychodrama for the purposes of substance use lapse and relapse prevention training. The proposed skill practice/role training oriented application of psychodrama is not intended to replace the more traditional exploratory applications of psychodrama with substance use populations. Instead, the application of psychodrama proposed in this article is offered as a stand-alone clinical treatment modality designed to augment the overall lapse/relapse prevention curriculum of the drug and alcohol rehabilitation treatment. The particular emphasis of the proposed psychodrama for use prevention is on minimizing the dysfunctional spontaneity with which substance use clients are left to improvise their way through recovery-challenging situations. Whereas Moreno's Theater of Spontaneity served the purpose of exploration of inter- and intra-psychic realities of the participants, the proposed Theatre of Relapse Prevention is intended to be used as a means of internalizing a behavioral algorithm of relapse prevention through the modality of psychodramatic role-play.

References

Avrahami, A. (2003). Cognitive-behavioral approach in psychodrama: discussion and example from addiction treatment. The Arts in Psychotherapy, 30, 4, 209-216.

Brook & Spitz (2002). The Group Therapy of Substance Abuse. Haworth Medical Press.

Coombs, R. H., & Howatt, W. A. (2005). The Addiction Counselor's Desk Reference. Wiley.

Corsini, R. J. (1955). Historic background of group psychotherapy: A critique. Journal of Group Psychotherapy, Psychodrama and Sociometry, 8, 219-225.

Dayton, T. (2003). Psychodrama and the treatment of addiction and trauma in women. In Gershoni, J. (Ed.), Psychodrama in the 21 century: clinical and educational applications. Springer Publishing Company.

Feasey, D. (2001). Good practice in psychodrama: An analytic perspective. Whurr Publishers.

Frances, R. J., Miller, S. I., & Mack, A. H. (2005). Clinical Textbook of Addictive Disorders, Third Edition. The Guilford Press.

Garcia, A. & Buchanan, D. R. (2000). Psychodrama. In Lewis, P. & Johnson, D. R. (Eds.), Current approaches in drama therapy. Charles C. Thomas.

Kellerman, P. F. (1992). Focus on psychodrama: The therapeutic aspects of psychodrama. London: Kingsley Publishers.

Landy, R. J. (1997). Drama therapy – the state of the art. The Arts in Psychotherapy, 24, 1, pp. 5-15.

Lipman, L. (2003). The triadic system: Sociometry, psychodrama, and group psychotherapy. In Gershoni, J. (Ed.), Psychodrama in the 21 century: clinical and educational applications. Springer Publishing Company.

Petruzzella, S. (2004). Introduction to dramatherapy: Person and threshold. Brunner-Routledge.

Rustin, T. A. & Olsson, P. A. (1993). Sobriety Shop – a variation on Magic Shop for addiction treatment. JGPPS, Spring, pp. 12-23

Woodward, G. (2004). Acting for change: The evolution of a psychodrama group. In Reading, B. & Weegmann, M. (2004). Group psychotherapy and addiction. Whurr Publishers Ltd.

Choice Awareness Training

"Freedom to Change" Variable in the Equation of Recovery and Choice Awareness Training in the Context of Substance Use Treatment

Abstract

The article introduces a tri-partite change equation consisting of the following three change variables: freedom-to-change, reason-to-change, and method-to-change. The freedom-to-change construct is conceptually differentiated from the construct of self-efficacy, and is operationalized through Choice Awareness Training. Choice Awareness Training, which involves a combination of Logotherapy and modified Mindfulness training, is introduced as an element of the overall clinical curriculum for substance use and compulsive spectrum clinical presentations. The article reviews a curriculum of discussions and exercises designed to challenge cognitive-behavioral automaticity and freedom-restricting belief schemas that constitute phenomenological barriers to one's perceived freedom-to-change. The article concludes with a sample of qualitative evaluative data from client participants obtained from a 2002-2003 pilot of Choice Awareness Training in the context of a residential, correctional drug and alcohol treatment program in an American jail.

From Psychology of Disease to Psychology of Choice

Compulsive behavior is, by definition, experienced as being un-free: a substance user feels compelled or driven to use. Compulsion, at a certain level of analysis, is experienced as a state of being enslaved in a pattern of repetitive behavior. This forced, driven, un-free nature of the compulsive experience is reflected both in the etymology of the cattle-prodding verb "to compel" (from the Latin compellere "to drive to-gether," from com- "together" + pellere "to drive") and in the experien-tial accounts of loss of control with its corresponding DSM-IV diagnostic criterion of "unsuccessful efforts to cut down or control substance use" (APA, 1994). But who is this invisible driver that shepherds (sheep-herds) the addicted mind? What is this presumed ominous entity that takes over the steering wheel of human volition to drive us into a functional abyss as we take the backseat to our appetites and drives? Is addictive behavior really compulsive, in the sense of being driven by an external force that is outside of our control? Or is addictive behavior nothing more than a choice that has become a habit?

How one answers these questions (if such questions are even posed in the still expanding days of the Disease Model reductionism) determines the therapeutic ceiling of recovery. A person who might have previously thought that he or she chose to engage in the appetitive behavior but who has eventually come to conceptualize such behavior as being compulsive, has, in a sense, shifted away from the ontological position of free will (a responsible stance of driving) and internalized a position of existential passivity and determinism (a victimized stance of being driven).

With this in mind, a key humanistic challenge of recovery from substance use and other compulsive spectrum disorders appears to be a recovery of one's sense of freedom to choose, to act freely, to determine one's behavior, and to control the controllable aspects of one's life. And, indeed, without a regained sense of freedom-to-change, how can a journey of change even begin? Change, after all, is psychologically predicated on a perceived freedom to choose a novel path, an alternative course of action, a different way. Recovery from compulsive behavior without the recovery of one's sense of control and agency is behavioral rehabilitation without existential rehabilitation. The proponents of the Disease Model of addiction (that, on inspection, is nothing more than a reified metaphor) are at least consistent: when viewed through the deterministic lens of incurable disease, one can never be recovered. Indeed, if we diagnostically define addiction as being accompanied by a sense of loss of control, treatment that only eliminates the compulsive behavior without reinstating a sense of control falls short of recovery and is nothing more than symptom management.

The Disease Model of Addiction and the Decline of Will

Allen Wheelis in his 1958 book, The Quest for Identity, sounded a civilization-wide bell of alarm as he wrote about the emerging "decline of will" (p. 42). Wheelis noted that "since Renaissance, man's sense of freedom has increased to a point probably unequalled in any prior civilization, achieving such expressions as 'I am the master of my fate; I am the captain of my soul." But as the "material universe" was found to be more and more "rigorously determined," "the concept of will has passed into partial eclipse." Wheelis noted that as an ever-growing number of patients doubted "the efficacy of will," so did the clinicians that treated them: after all, "the same culture produces both" (pp. 43-44). As the term "will-power" – among the clinically "sophisticated" – has become an "unambiguous badge of naiveté," one's attempts "to force one's way out of a conditioned of neurotic misery" became an unadvisable "counterphobic maneuver" (p. 44). What used to be a strength became a weakness, and viewing the controllable behavior as symptoms of an uncontrollable and incurable disease of addiction became a cure-all. A confession of a disease of addiction as panacea? Powerlessness as power? What paradox! In what could be seen as prophetic anticipation of the reign of the Disease Model of addiction, Wheelis remarked: "in our understanding of human nature we have gained determinism and lost determination – though these two things are neither coordinate nor incompatible."

Bruce Wilshire, in his 1998 book Wild Hunger: The Primal Roots of Modern Addiction, writing forty years after Wheelis, echoes the same existential sentiment: "to regard addiction as a disease is well-intentioned, but it is a de facto insult to human beings," and adds that the "great price" of viewing addiction as "something that happens to us" is the loss of one's sense of freedom, of "the immediate sense of oneself as an ongoing source of initiatives in the world, a real power, an agent" (p. 97). What does Wilshire possibly mean by the "well-intentioned" mandate of the Disease Model? In trying to combat the moralizing of the Temperance view of substance use as sinful, the Disease Model medically mainstreamed substance use treatment and, thus, spared legions of substance users from the moral scorn of society. But in this unmistakably humanistic attempt to extricate chemical coping from the shadows of "sin," the Disease Model overshot: the "baby" of human self-determination, agency, freedom and will has been thrown out along with the "bathwater" of moralizing.

It is a philosophical banality to say that there is no freedom without responsibility. Applied to the challenge of substance use treatment, it would seem just as banal to proclaim that there can be no recovery of a sense of control as long as the prevailing treatment ideology externalizes one's free choice (to engage in a given behavior) to the specter of disease. It would seem that to view substance use as conditioned, habitual, self-medicating, self-regulatory, coping behavior is intuitive, but apparently it is not. Many have tried to ram the "well-intentioned" bastion of the Disease Model with facts and eloquent argumentation: Stanton Peele (with his 1989 Diseasing of America), Glenn Walters (with his 1999 The Addiction Concept), Jeffrey Schaler (with his 1999 Addiction is a Choice). But seemingly to no major avail. Peele, Walters and Schaler aren't some clinical Stoics peddling "can-do" spirit. These are compassionate clinicians trying to advocate for their patients' most inalienable psychological right, the right for self-determination.

So, then, what's the matter? Why haven't these books resulted in a humanizing reform of the recovery industry? The problem might have to do with the fact that the addiction-as-a-choice model is experientially counter-intuitive. "If I can quit, then why haven't I quit?" – this sentiment, unless unaddressed, is the stumbling stone of the addiction-as-a-choice model. Peele, Walters, and Schaler, if we may extrapolate from their writings, are philosophically versed thinkers who are onto-logically and strategically convinced of free will. Yet the majority of the patients seeking help with problematic substance use are preoccu-pied with tactical goals: they are in search of immediate symptom relief and, as such, are not attuned to the fundamentally existential context of their presentations. A sense of loss of control and feeling compelled to use, i.e. feeling experientially un-free and enslaved by compulsion, is a quintessential issue of existence. To rehabilitate behavior and to fail to rehabilitate the perceived loss of control is to ignore the phenomenological heart of the matter.

This is where Logotherapy (Frankl, 1969) comes in. While Lo-gotherapy is uniquely positioned to address the existential subtext of such substance-use related concerns as perceived loss of control (Somov, 2007), the clinical proponents of the addiction-as-a-choice model run the risk of putting their clients on the defensive when they begin with the conclusions of their philosophical musings, rather than from the beginning, with a Socractic style discussion of the underlying concepts. The ontological journey from the perceived loss of control to re-conceptualizing addiction as habitual mindlessness and re-conceptualizing recovery as re-gaining a sense of control (as well as behavior modification) has to commence at the beginning, with the validation of the sense of loss of control. A habitual substance user does, indeed, feel that he or she has no choice but to use. This feeling of being un-free, of course, does not negate the fact that the user is technically free to act as he or she pleases. But, to resort to another philosophical banality, perception is reality; and it is the task of the clinician to assist the client to go beyond this perception of being un-free by discussing the psychology of freedom which is the psychology of choice awareness.

Psychology of Freedom, Choice and Change

Psychology of freedom, psychology of choice, and psychology of change are irrevocably intertwined since freedom manifests through awareness of a choice and since there can be no change with a choice to think or act differently. The notion of "choice" refers to: a) the aware-ness of there being two or more options available to choose from, and to b) the act of selection of one of the options available. The perceptual awareness of options is what gives us a sense of freedom. The behav-ioral act of selection of options is the process of change. Restated, choice is both an awareness of options that creates a sense of freedom, and an act of selection of the option that constitutes the fact of change. Therefore, freedom-to-choose is freedom-to-change.

The Change Equation

The Change Equation, or the Motivational Enhancement, Choice
Awareness, and Use Prevention Therapy (Somov & Somova, 2003), is
a proposed algorithm of change intended as a theoretical platform for
the treatment of the compulsive/addictive spectrum of psychological
presentations. The mandate of applied psychology is that of facilitating
change, from one state to another. The Change Equation proposes the
following "equation" of change: Change = Freedom to Change +
Reason to Change + Method to Change. The Change Equation model
begins with the thesis that a sense of freedom to change is primary:
one has to recognize oneself as being free (i.e. capable) in order to
endeavor a change. While reason to change (motivation for change) is
important, it is at best predictive of an attempt at change. Method to
change (which involves the mastery of change-specific skills such as
craving control or emotional self-regulation) serves to predict the
successful maintenance of change once it has been endeavored, but
only if the person remains aware of the choice to utilize the skills
whenever necessary.

Barriers to Agency: Automaticity and Freedom-Restricting Schemas

The Change Equation model recognizes that a sense of being free to
change (agency), while an ontologically inalienable constant, is a
perceptual variable. And indeed, while, in theory, at any given moment, we have at least two or more options (or degrees of freedom) to

choose from, we often feel that we have no choice. In other words, while the fact of our actual freedom is a constant, our perceptual freedom is a variable that is limited by cognitive-behavioral automaticity and freedom-restricting belief schemas. Cognitive-behavioral automaticity is thinking (interpretive) and acting habits, i.e. schematic reactivity that is devoid of conscious awareness of response choices available at a given moment. Such automaticity results in mindlessness that "narrows our choices" (Langer, 1989, p. 55). Freedom-restricting belief structures (such as a premature cognitive commitment to the Disease Model of addiction) are maladaptive conceptualizations of the problem that restrict one's perceived capacity for change.

Total Freedom-to-Change: Strategic and Tactical Choice Awareness

Clients' sense of freedom-to-change is facilitated through Choice Awareness Training that involves cultivation of both strategic and tactical choice awareness. Cultivation of clients' strategic sense of being free is accomplished through a systematic challenging of clients' freedom-restricting belief schemas, and is designed to leverage an ontological shift to a baseline (strategic) realization that one always has a choice in any matter, that one cannot not choose, and that, as a result, one is fundamentally free, free to choose, and, thus, to change. Successfully instilled sense of freedom (to choose and, therefore, to change) has no "half-life" and offers an open-ended interpretive relapse prevention buffer against failed efforts at change.

Knowing that one is fundamentally free is only theory, however
empowering it might be. In practice, an operational, tactical of being
free manifests through choice awareness, i.e. through the awareness of
the options that are immediately given to us. If I am aware of no
options, then, phenomenologically, I have no choice, and, therefore, I
am not free since there is nothing to choose from. Thus, a here-and-
now awareness of options is a prerequisite for an act of choice and for a
corresponding sense of being free. This tactical sense of freedom is a
function of the number of consciously perceived options at any given
time out of all the potential options available to an individual in any
given moment. Consequently, tactical (actionable, realizable, pragmatic) freedom is directly proportionate to the degree of choice awareness: the greater the awareness of the choice options available at any
given moment, the greater is the degree of freedom.

In summary, from the standpoint of the Change Equation model
of change, in order for change to occur (assuming the reason to change
and the method to change), one must: a) become strategically aware of
one's fundamental freedom to choose, and, thus, to change; b) re-
conceptualize the perceived loss of control as being a function of habit-
associated automaticity, and c) develop a habit of being tactically aware
of the options available in any given moment, particularly at the times
of making change-relevant decisions which is facilitated through an
increased baseline of choice awareness with the help of daily choice
awareness practice. On a technical level, Choice Awareness Training
consists of a combination of Logotherapy (to promote ontological,
strategic, existential sense of always having a choice and, thus, being

fundamentally free) and modified Mindfulness Training (to promote tactical, here-and-now awareness of immediately given choice options). Choice Awareness Training was piloted in the context of a correctional residential drug and alcohol treatment program in an American jail, as part of an overall clinical curriculum predicated on the Change Equation model (Somov & Somova, 2003).

Freedom-to-Change and Self-Efficacy: Conceptual Differentiation

Bandura (1977) defined Self-Efficacy as a person's belief in (or confidence in) his or her ability to successfully carry out a specific task. Freedom-to-Change is a belief that one is fundamentally free to change, i.e. that one is free to perform or "can" perform a given task.

The "can-do-ism" of Self-Efficacy and the "can-do-ism" of Choice Awareness Training, as similar as they may seem, are fundamentally different issues. The "can-do-ism" of Self-Efficacy, with self-efficacy being defined as confidence in one's ability to succeed, is a probability of success issue, whereas the "can-do-ism" of the Freedom-to-Change is a capability issue. The Freedom-to-Change construct is designed to reflect the species-wide range of human capability (is a given endeavor within my human capacity?); whereas the construct of Self-Efficacy is a person-specific estimation of the probability-of-success (will I succeed at this endeavor if I were to attempt it?). With these distinctions in mind, the thrust of Choice Awareness Training is not to nurture the client's belief that he or she will successfully carry out a specific task, but to nurture the client's realization that he or she can carry out the task in question. With this distinction in mind, it could be said that the "can-do-ism" of Self-Efficacy is really a "will-do-ism."

This conceptual differentiation might seem like clinically insignificant hair-splitting. But it isn't: the difference between Freedom-to-Change (which delineates one's capability) and Self-Efficacy (which predicts the probability that a given action will be taken) is no less significant than the difference between capability and motivation. If treatment fails to differentiate between the constant of "capability" (can-do) and the variable of motivation-contingent "probability" (will-do), the individual, faced with a lapse or a relapse, is certain to attribute his or her failure to lacking "capability," i.e. to being globally unable and incapable to meet and maintain the recovery goals. This catastrophized "I can't do this!" conclusion will, unfortunately, take the place of an otherwise more self-accepting conclusion of "I know I can do this, but I have not yet succeeded in doing so."

From Freedom-to-Change to Readiness-to-Change

The transition through the initial stages of readiness-to-change (Prochaska & DiClemente, 1986) might be arrested by a client's sense of inefficacy. Miller and Rollnick (1991) recognized the need to enhance the client's self-efficacy (i.e. client's belief in his or her ability to successfully carry out the tasks of recovery) as part of motivational enhancement. Given the above-delineated distinction between self-efficacy and one's sense of being fundamentally free to choose, and,

thus, to change, it would appear that the ambivalence of the Precon-
templation stage might be just as much about whether one can change
as it is about whether one will be able to change. The "I want to, but I
am not sure if I can" ambivalence appears to be phenomenologically
precede the "I can, but I am not sure if I want to" ambivalence. And,
indeed, in order to motivationally vacillate as to whether one wants to
change or not, one would have to first presuppose that the very change
in question is even possible. Furthermore, a client who appears to be
motivationally ambivalent, i.e. seemingly unsure if he or she wants to
proceed with the tasks of recovery, might be merely questioning
whether he or she can, in fact, change. With these considerations in
mind, it is recommended here that Choice Awareness Training (as a
means to developing one's sense of Freedom-to-Change) should ideally
precede the cultivation of the Reasons to Change or, at the very least,
proceed in parallel with motivational enhancement.

Arguments of Spiritual Determinism in the Context of Choice Awareness Training

The content of Choice Awareness Training is non-faith-based. Any
religious or fatalistic remarks about pre-determined destiny, fate, or
God's will are to be respectfully re-directed. When such comments
cannot be disregarded and require attention, clinicians are encouraged
not to disagree but to reframe the notion of choice at a micro (moment-
by-moment, day-to-day) level, not at a macro (cosmic/spiritual) level.

Part I of Choice Awareness Training: Cultivating A Sense of Strategic Freedom to Change

This part of Choice Awareness Training can be conceptualized as a curriculum of themes, the discussion of which helps clients cultivate a strategic, philosophical, ontological awareness of their freedom as a fundamental human condition. This takes the form of a part-didactic, part-Socratic dialogue with the client about their capacity for choice, and, thus, change. The following are themes and exercises that constitute this part of Choice Awareness Training.

Reframing the Addiction as a Habit, not a Disease

Facilitators take clients on a conceptual head-on collision with the Disease Model of addiction. Addiction is reframed in the context of operant conditioning theory and the Disease Model of Addiction is challenged. This is accomplished through the review of the history of the Disease Model of addiction (for excellent coverage of these topics, please, refer to Peele's "Diseasing of America," Schaler's "Addiction is a Choice," and Walters' "The Concept of Addiction"). The logical inconsistencies of the concept of addiction as a disease and of the 12 Steps are reviewed. In particular, facilitators should be prepared to recognize the following errors in logic. Petitio principii is the logical fallacy of tautology in which the same premise serves as both the premise and the conclusion (Walters, 1999). Facilitators need to familiarize themselves with the tautology of the loss of control argument (in which the loss of control serves both to describe and explain addiction), the prediction tautology (a problem drinker can never drink in moderation and any drinker that can drink in moderation is not a problem drinker), and the denial tautology (any disagreement with the Disease Model of addiction constitutes proof of disease) (Walters, 1999).

Review of Self-Change Literature & of Client's Past Success Data

Clients are introduced to self-change literature, the study of the phenomenon of self-change among drug and alcohol users, an emerging empirical body of research that contradicts the postulates of the Disease Model of addiction. The self-change literatures helps address the logical fallacy of the argumentum ad verecundian (an argument that involves an appeal to authority to establish credibility, in the case of the Disease Model of addiction, this argument involves an appeal to medical authority, whereas in the case of the 12 Step paradigm, the argument involves the appeal to the spiritual authority of the "higher power") (Walters, 1999). Studies show that self-change "appears to be the dominant pathway to recovery" (Klingemann et al, 2001, p. 21). Facilitators present self-change statistics with a particular emphasis on the longitudinal stability of natural recovery.

Langer, in her 1989 book, entitled "Mindfulness," shares the results of a study that supports the importance of exposing individuals in recovery to various conceptualizations of recovery. In particular, Langer shares that in a study of forty-two patients attending an alcohol clinic, the individuals "who had been exposed to only one model of alcoholism" (early in their lives) "appeared to have developed mindsets so rigid that the options offered by therapy did not seem available to them," whereas "those who had been successfully helped in therapy virtually always came from the multiple role-model group" (1989, p. 52). Langer suggests that subscribing to a genetic/medical view of addiction constitutes a counter-therapeutic "premature cognitive commitment" to a particular model of recovery, and notes that "alco- holics who see the cause of their problem as purely genetic seem to give up the control that could help their recovery" (p. 51). Helping clients review the findings of self-change literature introduces alterna- tive views on recovery and safeguards against an unnecessarily fore- shortened clinical diagnosis.

Furthermore, clients who express skepticism about the validity of self-change literature are encouraged to explore their own self- change data. The clients' belief in their powerlessness over addiction is likely to be a function of a) iatrogenic ideological side-effects of past treatments that were informed by the Disease Model of addiction, and b) dichotomous/perfectionistic thinking that led clients to dismiss the partial success of their past self-change efforts. Facilitators explore clients' abstinence or harm reduction histories.

Discussing the Implications of the Disease-Model Explanatory Style

Individuals with a pessimistic explanatory style develop a sense of helplessness and give up in the face of failure or extreme challenge

(Satterfield, 2000). The disease concept of addiction is a paragon of the pessimistic explanatory style. The attribution theory research defines pessimistic explanatory style as a causal model that attributes the causes of a negative event to internal, stable, and global factors (Abramson, Seligman, & Teasdale, 1978). The disease model of addiction encapsulates all three. A sense of powerlessness, therefore, is a logical by-product of the pessimistic explanation of addiction as a disease and constitutes learned helplessness. Choice Awareness Training, in a manner consistent with positive psychology, helps clients appreciate that learned helplessness is not factual helplessness, and helps clarify the distinction between feeling helpless and being help-less.

Tackling the Issue of the Pre-Disposition

The notion of a pre-disposition is often misunderstood by clients. Pre-dispositions pre-determine certain needs, not the specific means with which these needs are met. If a person is predisposed for anxiety spectrum disorders, he or she has at least four options to self-regulate: 1) psychological self-help, 2) psychopharmacology, and 3) chemical self-help through substance use (as a form of self-psychiatry). Facilita-tors work to counter the fatalistic understanding of the notion of pre-disposition, reinforced by the fear-mongering Disease Model of addic-tion, and help clients realize that whatever pre-dispositions they might have, they are still fundamentally free to choose a particular method for addressing any biological, genetic, or chemical deficits that they might have.

Taking on the Issue of Addictive Personality

The notion of Addictive Personality failed to acquire empirical support in over half a century of scientific investigation (Miller and Rollnick, 1991). Clients are helped to see that the pathologizing connotation of "addictive personality" is merely a function of social stigma attached to a given appetite. Furthermore, with the word "addiction" seen in the context of operant conditioning, the very construct of "addictive personality" can be reframed as "habit-forming personality," which, of course, is universally possessed.

Countering the 12 Step Legacy of Powerlessness & Salvaging the Remainder of the 12 Step Ladder

Aside from discussing the limitations of the disease metaphor of addiction, the facilitators may also address the clients' experience of the 12 Step paradigm and what they have internalized about their freedom-to-change. East-West synthesis of Buddhist and Taoist thinking and modern psychotherapy offers a way to salvage the self-efficacy deflating idea of powerlessness, by reframing the surrender as a form of acceptance or letting go of one's attachment to the idea of being in control is power. Furthermore, the 1st Step of the 12 Step philosophy can be partially salvaged as follows. It is correct that individuals with substance use habits are powerless over preventing a stimulus-bound reoccurrence of their conditioned cravings. It is not however true that such individuals have no power over what to do with these conditioned cravings. It is also true that once intoxicated, a person's capacity to render effective, strategically-savvy decisions is debilitated to the extent proportionate to the degree and type of intoxi-cation as well as to the degree of one's metabolic processes and toler-ance. Consequently, a person is powerless to be his or her usual self when, in fact, he or she, due to intoxication, ceased to exist as an intact psycho-physiological entity that he or she is at a non-intoxicated baseline.

With these considerations in mind, the 1st, 2nd, and 11th Steps of the 12 Step approach could be reformulated as follows, if they are to be conceptually compatible with the philosophy of the current ap-proach. Step 1: "We admitted that we were powerless over having an occasional conditioned craving for drugs and/or alcohol, and that our minds had become unmanageable when we were intoxicated." Step 2: "We came to know that we, ourselves, could restore us to our func-tional baseline." Note that in paraphrasing step 2, it is recommended to replace the phrase "restores to sanity" with "restore to functional baseline." The term "sanity" implies that substance use is madness (rather than a form of, albeit imperfect, chemical self-regulation) and therefore retrospectively invalidates substance use as a legitimate, albeit imperfect, form of coping. To change, clients need a belief in their sanity. Implications of prior insanity only contribute to unneces-sary sense of hopelessness. After all, if past predicts the future, then past insanity predicts future insanity. Clients should not be robbed of their phenomenology as being rational. Finally, Step 11 can be salvaged as follows: "Sought through choice awareness practice to improve our conscious contact with ourselves."

Re-processing of the powerlessness legacy in such a way may allow clients with strong prior allegiance to the 12 Step philosophy to keep climbing the remainder of the 12 Step ladder while still preserving a sense of freedom to choose, and, thus, to change.

Discussing Habit Formation

If "addiction" is to be effectively re-conceptualized as a habit, not a disease, discussion of the process of habit formation is of paramount importance. Discussion of habit formation (of habit psychology) offers a normalizing, validating, explanation of how over-learned habits can lead to a sense of loss of control, without the counter-therapeutic externalizing that stems from the notion that has no control because of a presumed disease of addiction.

Habits have been often referred to as "second nature." The notion of "second nature" is a semantic gold mine that holds a phenomenological clue to the mystery of the sense of loss of control. Tengan (1999), in clarifying Lonergan's teachings on habit formation, notes that "a habit gives an inclination to an otherwise indeterminate potency (the will)," and, as a result, "predetermining us to act in certain directions" (p.97). Consequently, what was once a novel, mindful, idiosyncratic response pattern becomes an over-learned natural default.

Pavel Somov, Ph.D.

In its defaulted-ness, the acquired response pattern becomes automatic, it serves as an energy conserving short-cut. Barrett, as far back as 1911, likened the "automatism" of habits to a a state "arrived at by the will when it functions evenly, simply, and regularly in a manner more or less independent of conscious attention" (1911, p. 105-141). Llinas (2001), "a founding father of the modern brain science," writing ninety years later, used, instead, the term Fixed Action Patterns to describe modules of activity "that liberate the self from unnecessarily spending time and attention on every aspect of motor and non-motor activities" (p. 134). Llinas states clearly that the rationale behind Fixed Action Patterns is "the economizing of choices" (p. 144). Whether we refer to the habits as autopilots, or schematic behavior, or second nature, or learned behavior, or fixed action patterns, this automatization "liberates" us from having to make an infinite number of minute choices. As any default, this automatization spares the mind the work of any unnecessary deliberation or decision-making, thus creating the phenomenological sense of loss of control. In a sense, a "second nature" response pattern is experienced as "happening" to the person rather than "being executed" by the person. This kind of resource-saving automatization is a hallmark achievement of the human mind. Auto-piloting or automating of various cognitive-behavioral-affective routines enables human mind to multitask as it plows through the never-ending environmental bombardment of stimuli. The loss of the sense of control (or of the sense of agency) is the cost of this optimization.

As a side note, clients are offered to examine how their uncritical acceptance of the Disease Model of addiction, in a way, represents an attempt to economize. After all, the concept of a disease ("I am doing this because I am sick) is a simple emotional conceptualization to be contrasted with a cognitively harder concept of a habit ("I am doing this because I have been conditioned to do this").

Clients are helped to appreciate the fact that the momentum of the habit, its baseline behavioral orientation, its default inclination, its automaticity with its accompanying sense of "loss of control," does not, in and of itself, negate the underlying fundamental freedom to choose same or alternative course of action. As noted above, just because an action feels "out of control," it does not mean that it is, in fact, beyond control.

Lonergan described this momentum or force of the habit as the "antecedent willingness" or "unwillingness" to act in a particular manner. The "antecedent" qualifier in Lonergan's explanation is synonymous with an inclination or a default orientation towards a specific response, given a particular stimulus. The "antecedent will-ingness" is that phenomenological pull or drive or action-urge that predetermines a response. It should be noted and reiterated, however, that pre-determination does not equal determination. Tengan's (1999) use of the term of "voluntary habits" therefore can be understood as meaning that while, in retrospect, the execution of a habitual response might be remembered as an involuntary action, no habit is truly invol-untary since any habit can be voluntarily overridden by an act of free volition (p. 96).

Consequently, any habit can be likened to pseudo-involuntarism or pseudo-choicelessness, to coin a couple of terms. Explicit discussion of how habits are experienced as involuntary defaults while being entirely within the potential control of the individual is likely to produce a self-accepting sigh of relief when clients realize that they never lost the control but that they merely neglected it.

Discussing the Power of Context (the Placebo Effect)

Clients, indoctrinated by the Disease Model of addiction, may be both curious and stunned to know that the degree of intoxication is contingent on drinker's expectations and can be manipulated by modifying drinker's/user's expectations (Langer, 1989). On the basis of a review of many investigations, Langer notes that "thoughts may be a more potent determinant of the physiological reactions believed to be alcohol-related than the actual chemical properties of alcohol" (p. 183), and, in summarizing the findings of Shepard Siegel, Langer notes that "the failure of tolerance on the day of the overdose is a function of context," noting that overdoses are more likely in the unfamiliar environments. Langer summarizes: if context has the power to change both the degree of intoxication, the severity of withdrawal symptoms, and even the effect a drug overdose, then "addiction may be more controllable than is commonly believed" (1989, p. 184). Presenting clients with the discussion of the power of situational factors offers clients much food for thought as they begin to rethink the presumed medical determinism of their addiction.

Choice Moratorium Exercise

Facilitators are encouraged to inter-lace the "fiber" of philosophizing with the "desert" of exercises. One such exercise to offer is the Choice Moratorium. The Choice Moratorimu exercises highlights the inevitability of choice. Clients are challenged to not make any choices for a pre-specified period of time (e.g. one minute). The exercise is followed with processing of the clients' reactions and insights. For additional instructions for this exercise, please, refer to Somov & Somova (2003).

The "Gun-Point Test" Hypothetical

The "Gun-Point Test" hypothetical compliments the discussion of the claim that a client has no control over drinking or drugging. In this hypothetical, clients are asked to imagine a situation in which they have an intense craving and immediate access to the substance in question. For many users, not yet convinced of the power of choice and of their potential skill-power (of craving control), this moment is well past any feasible self-regulatory "u-turn." If they are this far into it, with the drug in their hand, many will tell you that they are well on the way to use. To complete the hypothetical, add the following twist: allow the clients to imagine that someone put a gun to their head and stated: "You use – you die." Ask the clients: "Would you use at this point?" Most clients, whether they will verbalize it or not, will admit to themselves that at a gun-point they would lay down the drug and walk away, not using it.

Ask the clients: "What does that mean?" Prepare to face the inevitable counter-argument that "Yes, but… in real life no one is going to hold a gun to your head and tell you that if you use, you die." Counter-argue along the following lines: "The gun – an inanimate object – did not introduce the choice not to use to your life, the choice was there all along, it's just that the presence of the gun helped you become aware of the choice."

Demystifying the Inanimate

Substance use clinicians often hear clients verbalize the aforementioned fatalistic attitude that "once I've got my hands on it ("it" here being the drug or the paraphernalia), I can't stop." This fetishist reverence for the object is likely a reflection of the stimulus value of the paraphernalia objects with their over-conditioned "pull" to use. As part of trying to "demystify the inanimate," to highlight the passivity of the inanimate matter and its inherent dependence on the human agency, the facilitator might drop a pen down on the floor and compare the pen to an object of paraphernalia. If the clients had been already offered Exposure/Response Prevention type craving control craving, the facilitator may more accurately simulate the moment by, say, opening a packet with sweetener and line it up on the table. The facilitator then discusses the intuitive physical reality of the fact that the simulated crack stem on the floor or the simulated line of cocaine or heroin on the table, in and of itself, cannot move or do anything on their own, let alone, control a human being. This seemingly banal discussion resets the chain of command: we, the humans, have power over the inanimate drugs and drug-related paraphernalia, not the other way around. It is the very breath that differentiates a human from a line of cocaine that is required for the inanimate substance of cocaine to become a substance use problem of a given human. This discussion often results in such revelations as "I gave it (the drug or paraphernalia) too much power, power that it doesn't really have over me." As obvious as this may sound to a non-using adult, the value of this kind of experiential "clarification" cannot be over-emphasized.

Addressing the Language Trap: I Can't vs. I Won't

In the first part of the Choice Awareness Training, explicit attention should be given to how substance use clients restrict their freedom-to-change with the wall of words. Language structures perception and perception, for all intents and purposes, is reality. The facilitators' task is to help clients appreciate the interplay of language and a sense of freedom-to-change. Case in point: individuals who have internalized the 12 Step dictum of powerlessness and bought into the Disease Model of addiction are prone to confuse the "I can't" with the "I won't." As part of Choice Awareness Training, clients are encouraged to become aware of the distinction. The "I can't" statement negates the availability of a given option. "I won't" is a matter of motivation. Whereas the "I can't" is an acknowledgement of not having a choice to perform a given act, the "I won't" is an act of choosing not to perform a given act.

For example, after instruction in and practice of craving control, clients will be assisted with understanding that while there is not a craving they "cannot" control, there might be a craving they "will not" control. While the former is an issue of choice awareness or skill-power, the latter is a function of motivation. Consequently, the fundamental distinction between the "I can't" or "I won't" is the difference in freedom-to-change and reason-to-change: while one might be free to change from one state to another at any given moment, one might not choose to change because one might not be motivated to do so. Confusing the "I won't" with the "I can't" is a process of self-deflation: each pseudo-"can't" diffuses one's sense of freedom and agency.

Discussing the Difference Between Difficult and Impossible

In facilitating client's understanding of the sense of loss of control, it is helpful to explicitly address the incremental progression of the sense of the control as the person attempts a self-stopping behavior after initiating a habitual response sequence. Zeigarnik (1938) demonstrated that a response sequence is harder to abort at the later sequence points of a given response than at the earlier sequence points. Baumeister et al (1994) clarifies with the example of a sexual response: "refraining from sex is undoubtedly much easier if one backs away after (or before) the first kiss than if one waits to intervene until after an hour of passionate necking" (p. 21). Clients should be helped to understand, however, that just because something is harder it is not necessarily also rendered impossible. Given the awareness of the proper incentive or disincentive (e.g. the Gun-Point hypothetical), a person regains the choice to disengage from the target behavior.

Summary: A Realization of One's Strategic Freedom-to-Change is Ego-Syntonic

Phenomenologically, the outcome of this semi-didactic, semi-experiential Logotherapy designed to help clients appreciate that they are fundamentally free, and, thus, free to choose to change, is an ego-syntonic sense of liberation and a regained sense of being once again possibly in control of their lives. This realization that one is free to choose and free to change is so empowering that once clients are provided with a logical framework to counteract the notion of disease-based determinism, they tend to hold on to this insight. In this sense the realization of strategic freedom-to-change is much like learning to ride a bicycle: once understood, it requires no additional practice and it has no expiration date. It is quite a different story with the tactical, here-and-now awareness of choices available to us in any given moment: the habit of falling existentially asleep and living on a cognitive-behavioral auto-pilot has to be replaced by a habit of waking yourself up. That is the task of the second part of Choice Awareness Training that is discussed further below.

Part II of Choice Awareness Training: Development of Tactical Freedom-to-Change

This part of Choice Awareness Training discusses the practice of
tactical (here-and-now, ongoing) choice awareness and development of
a daily Choice Awareness Practice as a way to potentiate change. The
true challenge of Choice Awareness Training is not necessarily the task
of helping the client awaken to their fundamental capacity to change
but to help the client weave that realization into the very fabric of their
life.

Choice Awareness Practice

The first part of Choice Awareness Training (facilitation of the strategic, philosophical, ontological appreciation for one's fundamental
freedom to choose and to change) can be accomplished within four to
six semi-didactic, semi-experiential sessions. The practice part of the
Choice Awareness Training was an ongoing treatment modality that an
inpatient substance use client availed himself of until the day of the
discharge from the program. As such, facilitated practice of choice
awareness (through the attendance of the Choice Awareness Practice
group and through corresponding choice-awareness clinical homework)
is recommended as an ongoing programmatic element in structured
drug and alcohol rehabilitation. The following is a discussion of how
an initially Logotherapeutic intervention designed to facilitate the
appreciation of the fundamental freedom-to-change transitions to a

form of modified mindfulness practice designed to institute an appreciation of the here-and-now opportunities for choice as well as to facilitate an "installation" of a personal choice awareness practice habit.

Choice Awareness Practice Group Session Format

Choice Awareness Practice (CAP) was originally designed as a group modality (Somov & Somova, 2003), as part of an overall clinical curriculum of group-based modalities, such as motivation-leveraging Logotherapy group, "Meaning of Life" (Somov, 2007), Relapse Prevention Psychodrama (Somov, in press), and others. While the description of CAP below is customized to group setting, Choice Awareness Practice is just as well-suited for individual applications. The CAP group, piloted in the correctional drug and alcohol treatment program, consisted of an ongoing discussion of the importance of developing a choice awareness routine interlaced with in-session practice of choice awareness that involve the practice choice awareness enhancing exercises. Choice Awareness Practice Group sessions consist of four potential elements: a) ongoing review of the rationale of the choice awareness change variable and of its interplay with other aspects of recovery; b) assisting clients with initiating and fine-tuning their daily choice awareness practice; c) helping clients process the experiential fall-out/insights from their increased choice awareness; and d) providing clients with an in-session structured choice awareness experience both to raise their level of choice awareness and to model ideas for choice awareness applications and practices.

Shifting from Strategic Awareness of Freedom to Examination of Tactical Barriers to Freedom

Having assisted clients with establishing their strategic awareness of their fundamental freedom to choose and change, facilitators begin to qualify the thesis of "you cannot not choose" by discussing various exceptions to this existential axiom.

While the strategic sense of freedom-to-change is undermined by the client's all-or-nothing view of their self-control attempts, as well as by subscribing to the choice-disempowering Disease Model of addiction and choice-incompatible language, the tactical freedom to change is undermined by lack of choice awareness, i.e. by habitual, schematic, stimulus-response, unconscious, mindless responding to internal and external stimuli. The overall goal of this section is to help clients realize that while they may be strategically free, they are not tactically free unless they are actively (or mindfully) aware of the choices imbedded in the here-and-now, particularly at various micro and macro crossroads of life.

Exploring the Barriers to Tactical Freedom

In exploring the barriers to Tactical (actionable, operational) Freedom, clients can be asked to ponder if there, in fact, some exceptions to the previously established existential maxim that "one cannot not choose." The following answers typically emerge, with minimal prompting: We cannot not choose unless we are: a) dead (given particular beliefs about the after-life or absence thereof); b) comatose, unconscious, or asleep; and c) acting on an impulse, reflexively, automatically, mindlessly, in a scripted, pre-programmed, pre-rehearsed, rote, conditioned manner, out of habit, without the awareness of the choice options available in a given moment. This type of discussion of the barriers to the tactical, in-the-moment, here-and-now awareness of choices primes clients for the metaphor of conditioned, habitual, mindless behavior as a kind of sleep, and for the metaphor of choice awareness and mindfulness as a kind of awakening. The metaphor of mindlessness as sleep existentially upgrades the mandate of Choice Awareness Training to a goal of self-awakening from the lull of automaticity.

Tactical Choice Awareness Training & Gurdjieff-Type Mindfulness Training

Long after the days of the Buddha, the utility of here-and-now, tactical mindfulness would be echoed by many of the philosophical and psychological brokers of the East. Few came as close to a practical choice-awareness training system as Georgy Gurdjieff, a charismatic early 20th century Russian guru, nicknamed the "rascal sage" (Speeth, 1989). Gurdjieff likened an un-awakened human being to a machine, self (personality) to a collection of habits, and awakening or self-understanding to, at best, a lucid dream, or an awareness of being asleep. Gurdjieff did not believe that un-awakened human machines phenomenologically experience choice and denied the human machine a power of self-determination: "We have no capacity to do, no 'free will' – in fact, no function of will at all" (Speeth, 1989, p. 33). Gurdjieff posited that "Man is born, lives, dies, builds houses, writes books, not as he wants to, but as it happens. Everything happens. Man does not love, hate, desire – all this happens;" a person does not choose: "the situation chooses" (p. 33). But, according to Gurdjieff, the human machine can study itself, and can develop a capacity for true will (Speeth, 1989; Ouspensky, 1949). Gurdjieff emphasized self-study through self-monitoring of one's motor-behavioral and cognitive-affective habits. More specifically, he prescribed such de-automatizing activities as assuming and holding of an uncomfortable sitting or standing position, the use of non-dominant hands to perform various routinized tasks of daily living, and modification of one's writing. Thus, Gurdjieff taught freedom from automaticity. Langer (1989), the author of "Mindfulness," writing at the end of the twentieth century echoes Gurdjieff's early twentieth century formulations and recommendations: "the automatic behavior," she writes, "has much in common with habit" (p. 16) and notes that acknowledges that "proper meditation techniques are said to result in a state that has been called de-automatization" and in a state of freedom from stereotypes and rigid distinctions (p. 78; Langer's italics).

But Gurdjieff, of course, wasn't the only one to write about automaticity. Wells, as far back as 1927, in her work entitled "The Phenomenology of the Act of Choice," observes the so-called "habitual" choices: "with repetition the development of the processes entering into volitional consciousness tends quickly to become habitual." (p. 92). Wells preferred the term "habitual" choices are really a misnomer since they involve no consciousness per se and are nothing other than cognitive-behavioral defaults, or automaticity. Wells, unlike Gurdjieff, apparently did not like the de-humanizing analogy to a machine, and felt that the term "habitual" choice, rather than the term "automatic," "better expresses the psychological constitution of the process" (p. 92).

Barrett (1911) did not feel he had to be apologetic about the terminology of automaticity as he saw it not only normal but adaptive: "automatism is the natural issue of normal motivation... a manifestation of the protective economizing tendency of volitional functioning" (1911, p. 141).

Gurdjieff drew a distinction between people who experience events as if they "happen" to them and those who are free. This semantic distinction between people who "do" and people for whom "everything happens" is tantamount to a distinction between choice-ful-ness and choice-less-ness.

It should be noted that the practical part of the Choice Aware-ness Training proposed by Somov & Somova (2003) was inspired by Gurdjieff's teachings and can be reasonably construed as a form of modified mindfulness training the purpose of which is to increase a baseline of here-and-now awareness of choices, as an existentially-prophylactic catalyst of habit-modification.

Choice Awareness as Modified Mindfulness Training vs. Classic
Mindfulness

While both Mindfulness and Choice Awareness Training are awareness
training technologies, the two are somewhat different in focus. Mindfulness is awareness, "awareness of simply what is" (Dimidjian &
Linehan, 2003). Choice Awareness is choice awareness, or awareness
of the opportunity for a choice and of self as a Chooser behind the
choices

Buddhist mindfulness is an awareness of the external object
with the purpose of assisting the meditator to eventually lose the sense
of being an observer and to unite in the moment, with the moment, in a
state of object-less, subject-less non-duality. Choice Awareness, by
definition, is an awareness of choice, an awareness of the fact that a
person has a choice (options at any given moment) and a capacity to
choose. Therefore, choice awareness does not aim to blur the boundary
between the subject and the object. On the contrary, it aims to reinforce one's sense of oneself as a subject, as a self-determining agency.
Therefore while mindfulness meditation represents a period of non-
judgmental observation passivity or non-doing, free of discursive,
interpretive inner narrative, choice-awareness practice is an active
process that infuses an awareness of choice into what was previously
automated, characterized with discursive self-narrating of the options
that one is tactically aware of and their alignment with one's strategic
goals. Whereas mindfulness is a state of accepting willingness (Di-

midian & Linehand, 2003), whereas choice awareness is a state of purposeful, psychologically healthy, and self-efficacious willfulness. In summary, mindfulness training is training in the awareness of being here-and-now, Choice Awareness Training is training in the here-and-now awareness of being free.

Demonstrating Automaticity, Mindlessness, and "Choice-less-ness"

The following are a few experiential ways to demonstrate automaticity, mindlessness, and "choice-less-ness" that can be used either as part of Choice Awareness Practice group or in the context of individual psychotherapy.

Pointing Out the Here-and-Now Automaticity

"Catch" clients in the middle of head nodding, leg shaking, and in the middle of their gestures. Point out the seeming mindlessness and automaticity of these motor behaviors. Help clients appreciate the fact that while they, in theory, had choices (about what leg to shake, how quickly to shake it, etc.), the behaviors "happened" on their own without there having been any conscious processing of the choice options or any conscious choosing. This type of immediate behavioral feedback is used to facilitate to a greater state of choice-awareness. As clients begin to become self-conscious, they, by definition, become conscious of their Selves: such moments of meta-cognitive self-

awareness and self-observation afford an empowering glimpse of the
dormant Chooser that is coming back "on-line."

Circle of Choice

Give clients four sheets of paper and have them draw a circle. Then, in
rapid succession, have clients draw another one on a separate piece of
paper, and another one on the last piece of paper. Following this, invite
clients to comment on the similarities of these three circles ("In what
ways are these circles similar?"). In most cases, the mindlessly drawn
circles will reval a range of similarities on the following parameters:
clock-wise or counter-clock-wise direction of the circle, its diameter
(large, small?), its relative position on the page (centered, up or below
the center line?), and its starting point (twelve o'clock, three o'clock?).
Ask clients if they consciously intended for these similarities to occur
or if these similarities just happened. Ask them to ponder what that
means. Following this discussion of mindlessness and automaticity,
have clients draw a fourth circle, this time making conscious choices of
where to start the circle, which direction to draw it, consciously choosing its diameter size and consciously choosing where to place it on the
piece of paper. Have clients discuss how the experience of mindfully
drawn circle differs from the previous experience of mindless drawing.
Highlight any statements that indicate a sense of presence, a greater
sense of control over the drawing. In discussing the experience of
mindful circle-drawing some clients might convey a sense of being
somehow alert, awakened, and attentive. Ask the semi-rhetorical
question: "What if you could be this alert, this attentive and thoughtful

at a baseline, with matters and events that have much impact on your life?"

The choice of a circle as a figure to highlight mindlessness is not a random one in this case, and the facilitator is encouraged to capitalize on the metaphorical and existential significance of a circle as a metaphor for mindlessness. After all, what makes a "vicious cycle" vicious is its circularity. Help clients appreciate that motor-behavioral and cognitive-affective habits are in essence circular stimulus-response patterns of "always doing the same thing without realizing it." Most substance use and compulsive spectrum clients readily relate to the phenomenological entrapment of being caught up in a repetitive cycle of doing the same thing over and over again, despite the sincere intent to break out of this behavioral loop.

Congratulating for Choices Made

As a means of highlighting the fleeting and subtle phenomenology of the actual act of choosing, the facilitator are encouraged to rely on their observation skills and congratulate clients for any apparent novel choices. Note that the emphasis in this technique is on the fact of a conscious choice rather than on its rationale. With this mind, clients are helped to transition from the perspective of content-based assessment of choices to a perspective of assessing the choice in terms of whether it was a true, conscious choice or a pseudo-choice, i.e. a stimulus-response reflex. Thus, the only "bad" choice is the choice that is not made.

Processing of the Meaning of the Word "Just"

While facilitators refrain from judging client's choices, they are encouraged to inquire about whether, in the client's own opinion, a given
choice, if in fact consciously made, is in line with his or her treatment
goals. Thus, clients are helped to appreciate the fact that a choice does
not exist in a vacuum but is, in fact, indicative of the underlying
motivations which maybe current and up-to-date or existentially outdated.

Processing the meaning of the word "just" is one way to help
clients learn not to confuse mindless actions with choice-based actions.
Clinicians should be careful to make sure that this exercise is not
experienced as a form of picking on the seemingly benign behavioral
moments. To preempt the defensiveness, clinicians should introduce
this clinical moment in explicit terms as a choice awareness exercise.
For example, by asking a client's in a choice awareness practice group
about the rationale for his or her sitting position in the room, you are
likely to hear a defensive "just" of "I just decided to sit here." Patiently
and non-reactively assist the client with the realization that by saying
that he "just" sat there, he is, fact, saying that he sat in a given place for
no particular reason and is, thus, in Gurdjieff's terms, claims that his
behavior "just happened," without any conscious participation from
him. Therefore, paraphrasing the word "just" as meaning "for no

reason," the client is helped to appreciate the paradox of the moment: nothing happens without a reason and yet it somehow "just" did.

By inviting clients to unravel the mystery of clients' seemingly uncaused ("just happened") behavior, facilitators work to demonstrate how the behavior, even when not consciously chosen in the present, reflects possibly outdated motivation that might be in conflict with current recovery goals. These "just-s" can be also related to what Marlatt & Gordon (1985) referred to as "seemingly irrelevant decisions" that may lead to a lapse or a relapse. Consequently, clients are helped to see the potential role of choice awareness in relapse prevention.

The Arbitrary Choice: Practice of Spontaneity

If you were to be asked "What would you rather have: red or blue, one or one point three, a glass or a cup?" you would probably respond with a degree of annoyed bewilderment: "Red or blue what? One or one point three of what?! A glass or a cup of what?!" While this "offer" appears meaningless it is not without some choice awareness training value. Such offers represent the opportunity for a pure choice. If you were to be offered a $20 or $100 bill, "no strings attached," your choice would be more or less predetermined by the pragmatics of financial common sense. Presenting a purely arbitrary choice, on the other hand, is challenge to common sense and pragmatics, and, as such, is a valuable opportunity to "wake up" and make a conscious choice.

In choice awareness practice, facilitators may offer clients meaningless choices that cannot be guided by the previously conceived considerations of pragmatics, commons sense, or value. Such un-motivated choices, in a way, represent what Tillich (1952) referred to as "freedom beyond freedom," an ultimate manifestation of spontaneity. A spontaneous choice is free the logic of the past. In its freedom from historical pre-determination, such choice has no past to rely on and, thus, can only rely on the here-and-now assessment of one's motivation, which requires presence and awareness. Evaluation of two equally meaningless options results in a choice of the purest kind. The capriciousness, subjectivity, irrationality, moodiness, unpredictability of such a choice highlights our freedom to choose in a manner that does not have to reflect our socio-economic, socio-cultural, and psycho-biological predispositions.

Who's Doing It?

The "Who's Doing it?" choice awareness exercise involves a simple task of repetitious execution of a motor behavior. For example, the facilitator may ask the client to clench his fist, but only after consciously choosing to do so. The facilitator tells the client: "clench your fist only after you have made a conscious choice to do so each and every time, and do that for a while." As the facilitator observes the client, he or she suggests that the client speed up the pace. Clients are likely to notice that they are able to increase the pace but they are not necessarily able to match the increased pace of the motor behavior with the pace of conscious choosing. In a manner of speaking, at a certain speed of behavior, they allow the behavior to begin to "happen" without consciously initiating it. Facilitators invite clients to process this experience in terms of their experience of choice and automaticity. Facilitators may also engage the client while the client is continuing with the exercise and ask: "Who's doing it? Who's clenching your fist while we are talking?" This demonstration of automaticity-on-demand is discussed in terms of our capacity to self-program, and, thus, self-reprogram, and its pro-recovery habit-formation value.

Arbitrary Abstinence and Arbitrary Maintenance

Gurdjieff encouraged his students to give up "something valuable" but "not forever" in order to create a constant "friction between a 'yes' and a 'no'" (Ouspensky, 2000, p. 45). This suggestion offers a valuable choice awareness training opportunity as long as it is not misconstrued as an exercise in Stoic asceticism. Arbitrary Abstinence and Arbitrary Maintenance exercise is an opportunity for clients to practice both making choices (of what to quit and what to start), and serves to also hone their craving control skills for resisting temptations. In recommending this exercise as a choice awareness practice clients are emphatically encouraged: a) to make only arbitrary choices about what to quit and what to start, b) to commit to a pre-specified, time-limited abstinence or maintenance (timelines should be initially short and plausible, i.e. a week or a month); and c) to feel free to break the commitment any time, if they wish to do so, as long as this is done via a conscious choice. Clients should be explicitly cautioned against misusing this exercise for dieting or going off medication and any other physiological parameters of their living that may jeopardize their health.

Demonstrating the Emotionally Pragmatic Appeal of Mindlessness and Automaticity

As part of Choice Awareness Training, the following "Word Choice" exercise can be used as both an opportunity to demonstrate the emotional pragmatism of choosing not to choose and as a choice-training exercise. Participants are instructed to repeat in their mind the word pronounced by the facilitator or to think the word opposite to the one pronounced by the facilitator. For example, as the facilitator says "black," clients will be saying to themselves the word "black" (same word choice) or "white" (opposite word choice). With these instructions clarified, the facilitator begins to say the words "black" and "white" in random order, and continues to do so for a period of one or two minutes. Following the exercise, the facilitator offers to discuss the experience. The theme to highlight is clients' attempts of trying to organize an otherwise chaotic stream of stimulation. Some clients will report that after a few moments of repeated stressful indecision they decided to always think the same word or to always think the word opposite to the one announced by the facilitator. The clinician facilitates the discussion of this dynamic, of its existential meaning and its parallels with substance use. In particular, clients are helped to appreciate the freedom-escaping allure of the self-imposed autopilot that represents a trade-off between the stress of conscious, mindful choosing and tension relief.

Following such discussion, the facilitator encourages clients to "claim" their freedom to choose, to not go on auto-pilot, to choose freely on a moment-to-moment basis, and resumes the exercise. This "Word Choice" exercise can be used repeatedly as a choice-conditioning, with the term "conditioning" here being akin to muscle conditioning. Methods for self-administration of this choice-conditioning exercises (such as making a recording with a random presentation of these word stimuli or involving a support person to work with the client) can be discussed as well.

Not All Mindlessness is Bad: Pro-Recovery Automaticity

The discussion of the potential benefits of mindlessness and automaticity allows clients to develop a balanced view of the pros and cons of being on an auto-pilot. It is paramount that clients avoid the sweeping generalization that all automaticity is unhealthy. Habits are necessary and essential for adaptation. Clients are helped to appreciate the utility of both change-facilitating and change-maintenance recovery habits. Clients are encouraged to recognize that by the very virtue of their participation in treatment they are choosing to "program" themselves to respond with a certain pro-recovery automaticity in the face of possible future challenges to their recovery goals.

Emotional Deepening: The Costs of Automaticity

Mindless, reactive, habitual, mechanical, schematic, rote, conditioned, fixed, rule-governed, impulsive, stimulus-bound, auto-piloted existence is not unlike being asleep or sleep-walking, at best. This can be a rather existentially-poignant and, thus, motivationally-enhancing realization: most would be appalled at the notion of sleeping away their life. To deepen the appreciation for the need to be more awake and aware, clinicians can offer a kind of existential accounting to help clients ballpark how much conscious time they have actually lived (by factoring out actual nighttime sleep and conditioned sleep of mindless-ness that pervades our lives). Pushing the existential button of time loss allows the facilitator to heighten clients' motivation for the need to wake up and to stay awake, if they are to live as themselves, prudently apportioning time, their only existential resource, to what, indeed, matters.

Daily Choice Awareness Habit: Setting an Alarm-Clock for the Mind to Awaken the Sleeper

By this point in Choice Awareness Training, clients realize that know-ing the value of choice awareness does not make one choice-aware. An existential sleeper is asleep and is unaware of that fact and, short of outside help, will remain asleep. While counting on others to rouse oneself from cognitive-behavioral auto-pilots is certainly possible (through therapy and/or self-help meetings that remind one of his or her goals and priorities), learning to wake yourself up to the here-and-now freedom to choose and to change is the ultimate goal of Choice Awareness Training. Gurdjieff offered an elegant self-help solution for this problem. He believed that "it is possible to change certain aspects of overt behavior and to use such changes as reminders for flagging attention" (Speeth, 1989, p. 77). In particular, Gurdjieff suggested that an individual can set up a kind of mental alarm-clock that would awaken the individual continuously throughout life, at various selected time-points (Ouspensky, 1949).

Gurdjieff's suggestion, in the context of Choice Awareness Training, takes the form of cultivating a habit of de-constructing and consciously re-constructing various habits of daily living as an opportunity to infuse choice awareness into various routines of daily living. On a practical level, the client might begin with de-constructing their evening hygiene, re-sequencing its various steps, and including such "choice awareness twists" and mindfulness-raising alterations as brushing with a non-dominant hand, brushing and washing with one's eyes closed, making a conscious choice to not use the mirror on occasion, etc. For weeks, if not months, the client consciously varies his or her evening hygiene routine until he or she either tires of it or the new routine begins to feel old (i.e. too familiar to be of choice-awareness and mindfulness-facilitating value). At this point, the client makes a conscious choice to target a new daily habit. Once the client appears to have exhausted all available targets, he/she can recycle the previous targets. The opportunities for anchoring choice awareness in one's daily routines are practically limitless.

Helping Clients Select a Target for Daily Choice Awareness Practice
In selecting a choice awareness practice clients are encouraged to consider habits that are high in frequency and are likely to occur on any given day of a client's life regardless of circumstance and surroundings (such as hygiene routines, for example). Furthermore, it is recommended that clients try to anchor their choice awareness practice in high-frequency that are also reasonably paced throughout the day (e.g. mindful, choice-aware eating).

Portable Choice Awareness Practice

Conscious drawing of a circle (see more detailed explanation above) is recommended as a portable choice awareness practice that can help clients both internalize the metaphor of the self-reinforcing circularity of habits and provide an easy, on-the-go meditation on choice awareness.

Chess as a Choice Awareness Practice

Chess, as a game of strategy, is an excellent choice awareness game: it offers substance use clients a practice of ongoing evaluation of choices in terms of their consequences. Much of the behavior of substance use (and of the compulsive spectrum behavior) is tactical in its impulsivity, driven by short-term, immediate gratification. Chess teaches delayed gratification and, thus, impulse control. Chess, therefore, proves to be a viable anti-dote to tactically myopic compulsive functioning and prompts a player to evaluate the strategic ripple effects of any given choice.

Chess is also a rare interpersonal opportunity for silence and offers practice opportunities for emotional self-regulation of the emotions associated with victory or defeat. Finally, it is one of the few games that offers more than a binary/dichotomous outcome of win or lose. With its possible outcome of a tie, the game highlights the notion that not every form of competition is a zero sum game.

But above and beyond these already built-in choice-awareness and psychologically invaluable teaching moments, chess can be turned into a power-tool for choice awareness with a little bit of "tweaking." The following is a description of how chess was piloted as a choice-awareness enhancing tool in the context of the correctional/residential drug and alcohol treatment program. Upon admission, clients were provided with a brief overview of the choice awareness enhancing properties of chess and were, consequently, encouraged to learn to play chess. Chess, as a game of skill, was programmatically endorsed over such games of chance as cards. Regular chess tournaments were held each week with the first and second place winners earning various program privileges or nominal gifts, in proportion to the resources, policies, and logistics of the correctional setting.

Having assured that the majority of the program clients have learned to play chess, the program staff introduced a Choice Awareness Chess Tournament which involved an arbitrary change of board rules.

For example, the knight and the bishop chess pieces exchanged functions. As a result, the players – who by now had arranged themselves in a natural hierarchy of regular chess competence – were essentially equated in their playing power. With the new set of rules, the most choice-aware player was the most likely one to win. As the clients progressed through the program, they continued to be presented, from time to time, with Choice Awareness Chess tournaments with ever-unpredictable arbitrary modifications to the rules of the game, with each tournament being conducted on a set of new board rules.

Choice-Awareness Chess Modifications

A variety of modifications to chess rules are possible. For example, it could be agreed, for the purposes of the Choice Awareness Chess tournament, that pawns are allowed to always move two squares, or that a pawn can take over a piece both diagonally and directly in front of it. Furthermore, contrary to the classic premium on time during chess tournaments, Choice Awareness Chess tournaments would set time minimums to encourage clients to play "slow chess" as yet another way of leveraging choice evaluation, impulse control and strategic thinking.

Choice-Awareness Chess Tournaments as a Follow-Up Intervention

Substance use programs may consider holding Choice Awareness Chess Tournaments as a form of clinical follow-up. Such events may be held on an ongoing basis and follow the format of a chess club. Such chess tournaments would be offered as a post-treatment self-help opportunity for the graduates and alumni of substance use treatment, and may be facilitated or autonomously run by former clients, with organizers surprise-announcing the modifications of the rules on the days of the tournament.

Evaluation: Clients' Reactions to Choice Awareness Training

The Choice Awareness Training, as noted above, was initially designed as a part of a comprehensive substance use treatment curriculum and was subsequently applied in the context of a residential correctional substance use treatment program that took place in a program-devoted pod/cellblock of a county jail in Pittsburgh, Pennsylvania. No quantitative evaluation of this treatment modality has been yet undertaken. The following are a sample of client statements about Choice Awareness Training. These statements are taken from a weekly newsletter ("The Weekly Fix") issued by the inmates that participated in the program in question. These reactions provide a touching glimpse into how these correctional substance use clients (most of whom had been previously exposed to the Disease Model of addiction and to the 12 Step programming) responded to the proposition that they are fundamentally free to choose and, thus, to change. It should be noted that the participation in the pilot program was not accompanied by any legal assistance in the form of early release or sentence reduction. It should be noted that The Weekly Fix was entirely produced by the inmate population and the program staff exercised absolutely no editorial control over this in-house initiative.

Inmate client J. K. (The Weekly Fix, Issue 1, at the beginning of the program pilot) reveals the paradigm clash: "I must say that the program here <…> is not at all what I expected. <…> I've been brought up being told that AA and NA were the only solutions for my drinking and drug using… The biggest difference leading me to problems is step one of NA… This step differs immensely from what is taught here. We have the power to choose to use or not… In retrospect I can see how my belief that I'm powerless is harmful to me. It was an easy way out. All responsibilities for the consequences of my using <are> avoided by this simple belief. In all actuality these consequences are a direct result of an active choice I made to get high. Time will tell if I can adapt to this new way of thinking or not. I believe I can."

Inmate client H. T. (as early as in the second issue of the Weekly Fix) begins to zoom in on one of the core ideas of Choice Awareness Training. In his article "A Really Old Habit" H. T. reframed his substance use from a disease to a habit: "Most of my life, ever since I can remember, I have had the habit of biting my finger nails. <…> I am now 39 years of age, incarcerated for another habit, this one being potentially life threatening." So, the denial of having a disease of addiction without the denial of the detriment of one's habit of substance use can, in fact, co-exist!

Inmate client K. W. (The Weekly Fix Issue 3) opens with an editorial entitled "Turning the Auto-Pilot Off:" "I believe the more aware you are, the better chance you have in recovery. Being aware of the smallest things can help: like how you dress, how you brush your teeth or how you tie your shoe laces can keep you from going back to sleep. <...> I've learned that when I am aware of my options, and take time out to weigh them, and see what fits for me, it seems to make it a better day. I'm not always going to make the right choices, but as long as I'm awake and aware, I can no longer be on auto-pilot or unaware of my actions." These thoughts are a clinical treasure trove.

In the same issue (The Weekly Fix 3), inmate client who anonymously runs the column "Fact or Fiction, by Someone,' challenges his peers: "Choice awareness practice keeps me switched off the auto-pilot. And makes me aware that there is a number of options available to me, and when I choose an option, it is chosen mindfully." This "someone" is obviously no longer another anonymous statistic of powerlessness in the Alcoholics Anonymous or Narcotics Anonymous, but a "somebody" aware of his power to choose and to change.

In the same issue (The Weekly Fix 3), J. S. H. announces the arrival of his agency with the following title: "I Have the Strength Within." He continues: "The power is within me. I realize that I can't look to others for 100% guaranteed support. <...> In recovery there might not be anyone there (for you) at all. In times of weakness, I need to search myself and then look to others." Note the wisdom: the client is sober that he can't solely rely on home groups, sponsors and support networks. His recovery is portable because it is based on his own strengths. Note that this is not reactive pouting to a lack of conjugal visit: the client is not dismissing others' help, but merely no longer willing to rely on it as an exoskeleton to carry his weight.

 The former anonymous "Someone," now a "Somebody," per his pseudonym, albeit still anonymous, offers a unique take on the Choice Awareness Practice exercise in the Weekly Fix issue 4: he offers a game of "Dare and Catch Yourself." For example, "dare – to try and break an old habit, to not keep repeating the words "for real… for real;" and "catch yourself – tapping or humming, reacting over and over in the same way, asking question that have already been answered." This "somebody" is certainly showing some (creative) mind. Choice awareness, by virtue of opening up new options, has the effect of opening up the mind.

Speaking of opening the minds: inmate client D. F. (The Weekly Fix, issue 5) observes – "It's kind of funny how our minds work." He offers a choice awareness prank. Ask a peer: "How do you spell "silk?" Then, ask: What do cows drink? The usual response will be milk. Then you say: that's what people drink, cows drink water." D. F. is catching on to the vulnerability of mindlessness. His writing echoes a sentiment that was frequently noted by clients: they were quick to realize that stimulus-bound mindlessness is rife for exploitation.

The Weekly Fix, issue 8: an alpha-male inmate client "G." champions a full-on head-on with the notion of addiction being a disease. "I am glad to have the confirmation that I don't have a disease. For a long time I subscribed to the disease concept of addictions. This came from a lot of cognitive distortions I've picked up from attending N. A. and A. A. meetings. I am not doomed! <...> I am truly excited to learn that there is another way of staying clean. <...> The more I learn, the more it makes sense to me. A big part of my life, my decision making process has been to act on impulse <...> almost as if I had no choices. Rational recovery introduces me to phrases like "auto-pilot," "choice awareness," and "self-regulation," along with plans for lapse and relapse prevention, just to name a few. (This) gives me a "wonderful opportunity" to flex my "choice muscles." Come to think of it: this is all I ever wanted to do in the first place." This "testimony" speaks for itself.

C. P. asks in The Weekly Fix (issue 11): "Have you chosen to be free?" The misleading simplicity of this question conceals this client's in-depth understanding of the issue at hand: freedom manifests through an act of conscious choice.

Inmate client D. F. (The Weekly Fix, issue 11), in a drawing entitled "Mind Garage," amidst the drawings of a bicycle, a lawnmower, a garden hose, and an oil spill, has thrown in a self-affirming pearl: a call out that reads "You are not a victim." D. F. carries the theme over to the next issue (The Weekly Fix, issue 12): in the same "mind garage," among the same objects, in the driveway, he writes: "Potential impact of the disease? Inescapable fate..." D. F., here, seems to be in the midst of spring cleaning of his "mind garage," getting rid of the clutter of the victim identity and the disease identity.

H. T. (The Weekly Fix, issue 13) proclaims: "Choice awareness expands our options. <...> I find that there are seemingly endless choices." Well said.

In the same issue, we learn of the identity of the anonymous "Someone" who began the rubric "Fact or Myth." Having initially signed off as an anonymous "Someone," and having then progressed to a still anonymous "Somebody," he finally reveals his identity: he is N. M. In challenging his peers, he asks: "Choice awareness is all about being told what to do... Fact or myth?" We can safely guess his answer. What remains a mystery is the progression from anonymity to reclaiming one's identity: could it be the effect of a humanistic treatment approach? One thing is for sure: N. M. took the responsibility for his penmanship. Nobody told him what to do...

D. F. (the "Mind Garage" author, in the issue 14 of The Weekly Fix) offers a very cogent insight: in an article, entitled "Preset Recovery," he writes: " I was listening to my radio the other day trying to find a song <...> and realized how used to the pre-set channels I was. So I figured: what a wonderful opportunity to practice my Choice Awareness, so I changed the pre-set stations. <...> Each and every day I am getting closer to not living a pre-set life." D. F.'s essay is a glimpse into a mind free of pre-set recovery dogma.

Issue 5 of The Weekly Fix has a telling and humorous cover element. You see the following text encased in a rectangle: "I made a choice to put a rectangle around these words."

Issue 16 features clear thinking from J. F.: "Some things are not comfortable when not run on an auto-pilot. <...> But with pain, there's gain. I need to exercise my choice muscles which make me mindful so that I don't limit myself with mindless decisions. <...> When you take the time to consciously look around at everything around you, there are many options and life is limitless." J. F., who also signs off on this article as the "3d Eye" has his vision back.

D. F. (in The Weekly Fix issue 16) shows the readers his new acquisition for his "Mind Garage:" "It helps to be willing to change." Indeed. M. H., in the same issue, shares: "When I come to jail I just get into the mix of things. <...> Then I get out and go right back to the same thing. It just becomes a cycle of using and coming back to jail. <...> This time I make a choice to use this time mindfully. <...> I know something is different this time. That something is me." M. H. here speaks of the revolving door of incarceration, but he might as well be speaking of the revolving door of the kind of recovery that takes the agent of change out of the equation of change. After all, what use would there be for M. H. in the equation of disease?

The editors of The Weekly Fix devoted the 21st issue to Choice Awareness Practice (which in the program was known by the acronym C. A. P.). The cover features a ferocious baseball cap, the bill of which is drawn in a manner of tooth-ful scowl. The text above the C. A. P. reads: "Put On a Mean Cap." The text below deciphers the in-house acronym: "Choice Awareness Practice – mornings, evenings, after-noon, nights."

Jumping ahead (for the interests of space) to the 32nd issue, we see the following thoughts by T. G.: "When I first heard about auto-pilots, the idea was to break them. By breaking them I slowly began to wake myself up. I found a lot of good out of becoming the thinker behind the thought. <…> I feel that this is going to be the one most important thing to keep me on top of my recovery."

Inmate client M. S., writing in the same (32nd) issue notes: "Before I never thought I had options <…> because I was in a deep sleep. I lived most of my adult life absent from my thoughts. <…> I have learned how to switch off my auto-pilot by doing two or three five minute choice awareness practices a day. It (practice) lets me be more aware and awake. <…> When I do some simple C. A. P. (Choice Awareness Practice), it lets me know that I am my own agent of change and that my life is up to me."

In reviewing the last, 33d issue of The Weekly Fix, at the very back of the issue we find an anonymous vignette entitled "Recovered or Recovering." The very phrasing of this item highlights an awareness of an option that for most of the participating clients did not phenomenologically exist. Choice Awareness Training is designed to help clients recover their sense of control, and with it their prognosis of recovery.

Conclusion

The aforementioned existential-humanistic approach to substance use and compulsive spectrum presentations is offered from the operating platform of Positive psychology, namely, from the position of capitalizing on free will as a fundamental treatment asset, and in sharp contrast with the pseudo-medical psychology of disease of addiction that has now for years misinformed the recovery industry. The authors proposed a view of addiction as a process in which the initially conscious choice to engage in an appetitive behavior becomes a habit. The authors posit that in order to reverse the process of addiction, clients should be assisted with re-infusing choice awareness into their otherwise automated, mindless, choice-unaware, habitual behavior.

References

Abramson, L. Y., Seligman, M. E. P., & Teasdale, J. D. (1978). Learned helplessness in humans: critique and reformulation. Journal of Abnormal Psychology, 87, 49-74.

Bandura, A. (1977). Self-efficacy: toward a unifying theory of behavioral change. Psychological Review, 84, 191-215.

Barrett, B. E. (1911). Motive force and motivation tracks. Longmans: Green & Company.

Dimidjian, S. & Linehan M. M. (2003). Mindfulness practice. In O'Donohue, W., Fisher, J.E., & Hayes, S.C. (Eds.). Cognitive behavior therapy. (pp. 229-237). Hoboken, NJ: John Wiley & Sons, Inc.

Frankl, V. (1969). Will to meaning: foundations and applications of logotherapy. New York: The World Publishing Co.

Jellinek, E. M. (1972). The disease concept of alcoholism. New Haven, CT: College and University Press

Klingemann, H. et al. (2001). Promoting self-change from problem substance use: practical implications for policy, prevention, and treatment. Dordrecht, the Netherlands: Kluwer Academic Publishers.

Langer, E. J. (1989). Mindfulness. Perseus Books, Cambridge, MA.

Llinas, R. R. (2001). I of the vortex: from neurons to self. Cambridge, MA: The MIT Press.

Lonergan, B. J. F. (1957). Insight: a study of human understanding. London: Longmans, Green & Company..

Marlatt, G.A., & Gordon, J.R. (Eds.) (1985). Relapse prevention. New York: Guilford Press.

Miller, W. R., & Rollnick, S. (1991). Motivational interviewing: preparing people to change addictive behavior. New York: the Guilford Press.

Molina, F. (1962). Existentialism as philosophy. Prentice-Hall, Inc. Englewood Cliffs, NJ.

Ouspensky, P.D. (1949). In search of the Miraculous. New York: Harcourt, Brace, & Co.

Ouspensky, P.D. (2000). In search of the Miraculous. Moscow: Fair Press

Peele, S. (1989). Diseasing of America: How we allowed recovery zealots and the treatment industry to convince us we are out of control. Jossey-Bass Publishers, San Francisco, CA.

Prochaska, J. O. & DiClemente, C. C. (1986). Toward a comprehensive model of change. In W. R. Miller & N. Heather (Eds.), Treating addictive behaviors: Processes of change (pp. 3-27). New York: Plenum Press.

Satterfield, J. (2000). Optimism, culture, and history: the roles of explanatory style, integrative complexity, and pessimistic rumination. In J. E. Gillham (Ed.), The Science of Optimism & Hope, Research

Essays in Honor of Martin E. P. Seligman (pp. 349-378). Radnor, PA: Templeton Foundation Press.

Saunders, B., Wilkinson, C., & Allsop, S. (1991). Motivational intervention with heroin users attending a methadone clinic. In Miller, W. R. & Rollnick, S. (Eds). Motivational interviewing: preparing people to change addictive behavior. (pp.279 – 292). New York: the Guilford Press.

Somov, P. G., & Somova, M. J. (2003). Recovery equation: Motivational enhancement/choice awareness/use prevention: An innovative clinical curriculum for substance use treatment. Imprint Books.

Somov, P. G. (2007). Meaning of life group: Group application of Logotherapy for substance use treatment. The Journal for Specialists in Group Work, 32 (4), 316-345.

Somov, P. G. (in press). A psychodrama group for substance use prevention training. The Arts in Psychotherapy.

Schaler, J. A. (1999). Addiction is a choice. Open Court.

Speeth, K. R. (1989). The Gurdjieff work. New York: Jeremy P. Tarcher/Putnam

Tengan, A. (1999). Search for meaning as basic human motivation: a critical examination of Viktor Emil Frankl's logotherapeutic concept of man. Frankfurt am Main: Peter Lang.

Tillich, P. (1952). The courage to be. Clinton, MA: Yale University Press.

Walters, G. D. (1999). The addiction concept: Working hypothesis or self-fulfilling prophecy? Allyn & Bacon, Needham Heights, MA.

Wells, H. M. (1927). The phenomenology of acts of choice: An analysis of volitional consciousness. Cambridge University Press, London.

Wilshire, B. (1998). Wild hunger: The primal roots of modern addiction. Rowman & Littlefield Publishers, Inc., Lanham, MD.

Wheeles, A. (1958). The quest for identity: The decline of the superego and what is happening to American character as a result. W. W. Norton & Company, Inc. New York, NY.

Empower & Re-Cover

This "vignette" appeared in 2008 MindStream blog.

Empower yourself out of your existential impasse by recognizing the Intrinsic Motivation in all you do and by respecting your subjective approximations of Objectivity as being the best of what is epistemologically possible...

Re-Cover your original Ego Wound with psychologically healthier, legally safer and socially sanctioned dressing of Coping...

For whatever this All means...

Take the 12 Steps and Sit Down: Overcoming the False Legacy of Powerlessness with Craving Control

This essay was first posted as a blog on www.psychologytoday.com in 2008

In my past work as a clinical director of a drug and alcohol treatment program in a county jail and in my current outpatient work with substance use clients I continuously come across a certain iatrogenic (treatment-related) legacy of powerlessness which stems directly from the 1st of the 12 Steps of the AA/NA philosophy ("We admitted we were powerless over our addiction - that our lives had become unmanageable").

I get it: admitting that you have a problem is a psychologically healthy thing. But admitting that you are powerless to solve it?! What a self-deflating stumble of a step to start a journey of recovery... What were Bill W. and Dr. Bob thinking?!

Perhaps, Bill W. and Dr. Bob were trying to pull off a bit of East-West synthesis? Perhaps, the thinking was that surrender or letting go of one's attachment to the idea of being in control is power? That passively accepting and witnessing the urge to drink (or use drugs) rather than directly fighting the urge head-on would be akin to psychological judo or jujutsu, the "soft method" martial arts that harnesses the opponent's strength and adapts to changing circumstance?

If this is the East-West synthesis that they had in mind, then, what a failure of articulation!

Perhaps, perhaps, perhaps...

Or, perhaps, this confession of powerlessness over addiction is nothing more than a failure to appreciate the psychology of a craving.

Let's take a look!

Just the other day, a guy I've been working with, who's been through the revolving door of the 12 step programs and who had decided to seek psychotherapy in addition to "working the program," triumphantly announces that he "did" the first step. Again!

Now, he's known about my approach to substance use treatment and he has showed himself to be an open mind capable of critical thinking. So he seemed entirely non-defensive when I asked him about what he meant when he "admitted to being powerless over the Disease."

Keep in mind that by now he and I have spent many a session working exclusively on craving control skills. He paused... and, with a sheepish smile, dared: "I am powerful over the Disease, Doc?"

You have to appreciate the weight of 12 Step dogma that he was trying to raise from! Had he leaked this hypothesis at a meeting or in a session with a 12 Step "recovery zealot" he would have likely been accused of being in denial, "slipping," or "lapsing." So, for him to even dare to think that he might be, in fact, powerful over the Disease took guts...

It's basic and axiomatic: if you've been drinking and/or using for any length of time, you'll have craving thoughts. Nothing you can do about that. They'll pop into your mind, uninvited, particularly, when you are around certain "people, places, and things" or when you are in a certain state of mind.

This is plain ol' Classical Conditioning stimulus-response. And indeed, a person who has been using and/or drinking develops numerous conditioned associations between various stimuli and his/her drug of choice.

Naturally, until such person gets used to ("habituates to") these stimuli (in his/her post-cessation, post-drug-use life), he or she will experience conditioned cravings. So, in this sense, up to a point, you are powerless to entirely prevent and/or eliminate craving thoughts from their initial occurrence (after having been exposed to drinking/using stimuli).

But...

But just because you are powerless to prevent the craving thought from occurring in the first place, it doesn't mean that you are powerless to manage or control this thought.

Bottom-line: you are not powerless over how to respond to these cravings, over whether to act them out or to manage them. In fact, the Buddhist mindfulness meditation has been researched, clinically piloted and increasingly mainstreamed into the craving control repertoire of the contemporary drug and alcohol rehabilitation programs.

So, how about this for a first practical step: step aside (from the craving thought) and sit down (in mindfulness meditation) to restore your mind to its non-craving baseline.

Let's review what we got here... Addiction is a habit. Habits are stimulus-response patterns. If you have had any given habit for some time, when you decide to stop, your mind will keep reminding you to engage in a certain conditioned response whenever you are triggered or exposed to certain stimuli. But just because, your mind reminds you that you used to do this or that in this or that situation, it doesn't necessarily mean that you are powerless to avoid doing this or that, once triggered. So, while you are powerless to completely avoid these mental reminders, these craving thoughts, you do have power to manage these thoughts (through good ol' self-talk or by merely witnessing these thoughts and controlling your experience through mindfulness and/or relaxation).

Now, take a look at the following equation (1).

Using/Drinking Episode = Access to the Drug + Desire to Use/Drink/Consume the Drug

In order for you to use/drink, two things have to be absolutely present: you have to actually have the booze or drugs in your immediate possession and you have to have an active, immediate desire to consume the substance.

For example, if I got some drugs on me but I've been pulled over for speeding, my desire to use is on hold. Right now, all I care about is to get back on my way preferably without a speeding ticket, let alone without a possession charge. So, even though I have immediate and direct access to the drug, I have lost my immediate craving to use. As such, there is no using episode.

Similarly, if I actually got busted for possession and now I am sitting in the county jail, and I got a "whopper" of a craving but no immediate access to drugs, there's not going to be a using episode as I have no direct, immediate means to satisfy my craving.

Or, say, I am sitting at home getting ready to shoot up. But then I think: I gotta see my PO (probation officer) tomorrow and pee in the cup. If my urine's dirty, the PO is gonna "violate" me and send me back to jail. So, here I am: I got access to the drug and I sure have a craving for it. But - based on my pragmatic calculations - I gotta wait till after I see my PO. So, I have the tactical motivation to control my cravings (even if I have no strategic, long-term commitment to recovery) and, if I have the skill-power to control the craving, the basic know-how of how to manage this moment of desire, I might just avoid a using episode (if only for a day).

Where's the unmanageable disease here? Which part exactly am I so fundamentally unable to control? So, even though I have direct access to the drug, by controlling my craving - albeit for an arguably myopic reason - I am able to avoid a using episode. No disease here: just applied, situational morality of avoiding adverse circumstances. Mere interplay of tactical motivation and craving control skill-power.

But what a laudable, promising self-regulatory precedent to build on! What a clinical treasure trove of the distinction between "can't control the craving" and "won't control the craving" to process and analyze!

What all this means is that in order to avoid a using/drinking episode, you have to either eliminate the access to the drug and/or to control the craving to use.

The former - elimination of the access to the drug - is a Stimulus Avoidance strategy best accomplished through a tried-and-true AA dictum of staying away from "people, places, and things."

The latter - elimination of the immediate desire to use the substance in question - is the Response Control strategy best accomplished through craving control.

It goes without saying that if you've been using for long, let alone drinking, avoidance of internal and external stimuli that may trigger a craving is simply impractical.

After all, even if you don't go to the block corner any more, you still got your cell phone. And even if erase your contacts on the phone, you still hear all about it wherever you go - at a meeting, in the movies, you name it... And even if you were to go on a 7-years-in-Tibet retreat, you still have your mind to remind you of the good ol' times, right?

So, the Stimulus Avoidance strategy, the strategy of avoiding access to the drug - let's face it - is limited. What's left - and that should be plenty enough - is craving control. If you work on cultivating a solid, no-nonsense craving control skill-power, you need no will-power or God-power, and you definitely have no need for this dubious relapse prevention scare-tactic of "powerlessness."

"What craving control methods are out there?" you might ask.

I am glad you finally asked: psychological and chemical.

Psychological craving control methods, in the descending order of my clinical preference, are Mindfulness (best, in my opinion), Relaxation (good), Self-Talk (satisfactory), Distraction (so-so).

Chemical craving control methods: you name it - from methadone to Cyboxin...

I can almost hear it: "Busted! Gotcha, sucka! You said "methadone," you said Cyboxin... See! See! It's a disease. A Disease!!! Not a habit! How can you be in control of a disease?!!! It's physical, not mental, don't you see?!!!"

I see, I see... I'll take an unpopular stab at this mind-body Cartesian non-sense in a minute... But for now, let me just reminisce a bit...

Back when I was running a non-12-step drug and alcohol program in a county jail, I'd get challenged on my assumptions (like above) all the time. In adrenaline overdrive for two years, at least, I had to fend off these Disease Model counterarguments from my inmate clients. There's nothing, nothing like Antisocials' thirst for justice... The energy, the righteousness, the hunger to stump the expert! I enjoyed that work greatly: it paid off: while imprisoned, many of these minds were admirably free...

So, back to this notion of disease... It's just, frankly, silly Cartesian mind-body dualism. Thoughts and feelings are real, they exist - there-fore, they have a chemical (physiological) signature in this three-dimensional reality. Of course! No one's arguing with this - it is banally self-evident. So, just because somebody can show you what your "addicted" brain looks like on drugs, it doesn't mean that your habit is a disease.

I might be in a habit of tearing up every time I see a picture of that couple - holding hands - leaping out of the Twin Towers on 9/11. Think about it: I see the image and have a sad thought, and my eyes make water! A thought in my mind results in water pouring out of my eyes! Some fleeting event in my consciousness and look at this mess: I need a tissue, my eyes are red. A change in the state of mind led to a change in the state of body. Mind and Body are the Twin Towers: they stand together and they collapse together.

Need another example? Okay, here's one. I took a leak but forgot to zip up my fly. Now, when a client (God forbid!) points this out to me, I have a thought: "Oh, man! How could I?!" A fleeting event in my consciousness - and my face, my face (!) reddens as I blush. A thought of embarrassment - and blood, blood (!) re-distributes its flow and floods my face... What the hell... Must be a case of... "emotional-vascular" disease...

This mind-body connection is so tight that it's time we took the hyphen from this "mind-body" dualism...

So, what am I getting at? What I am saying is that addiction is a habit, and as any habit, it is a stimulus-response pattern, and as any human habit, addiction involves both mind and body (or better yet, the un-hyphenated bodymind), and that there is no difference between mind and body, they are a one indivisible whole, so when you control one part of this whole, you control the other part of this whole. That's how the whole thing works - as a whole! That's why craving control can be achieved either through psychological or chemical pathways. All roads lead to Rome, don't they?

You might say: "but what about the withdrawal effects, what about tolerance?" Again, everything you feel or think or do, has a physi-cal/physiological manifestation.

If you want to have a sip of coffee, the thought "I want some coffee" translates into a complicated physiological cascade until this thought of yours eventuated in a motor behavior of your hand picking up a cup of coffee from a table and bringing it to your lips. If you drink coffee a lot, then eventually your *bodymind* adjusts to this ongoing and habitual intake of caffeine.

Namely (you are better off skipping this psychophysiological mumbo-jumbo straight from Wikipedia unless you've already had a cup of coffee yourself this morning): "Because caffeine is primarily an antagonist of the central nervous system's receptors for the neurotrans-mitter adenosine, the bodies of individuals who regularly consume caffeine adapt to the continual presence of the drug by substantially increasing the number of adenosine receptors in the central nervous system. This increase in the number of the adenosine receptors makes the body much more sensitive to adenosine, with two primary conse-quences. First, the stimulatory effects of caffeine are substantially reduced, a phenomenon known as a tolerance adaptation. Second, because these adaptive responses to caffeine make individuals much more sensitive to adenosine, a reduction in caffeine intake will effec-tively increase the normal physiological effects of adenosine, resulting in unwelcome withdrawal symptoms in tolerant users" (Wikipedia).

My point? Just because we are not consciously supervising all this psycho-physiological re-calibration, it doesn't mean that it is a disease. When I cry, I do not consciously direct my tear glands to produce water. Nor do I instruct my circulatory system to divert a pint of blood to my face when I feel embarrassed. That's just what happens. The Cartesian mind-body paradigm of modern medicine, particularly, addiction medicine, latches on to the fact that what we do has a physiological signature and imbues it with the significance of the disease.

Just because my body reflects the workings of my mind in the mirror of flesh it doesn't mean that these workings are independent and uncontrollable. To think of addiction as a disease (rather than a habit with a physiological signature) is to presuppose a ghost in the (human) machine.

You might object: "But don't you see, drug use changes the bodily chemistry... Haven't you read the very passage you posted from Wikipedia... See, here they say, the increase in the number of adenosine receptors... These are actual structural changes!"

Yes, they are, indeed, structural changes. Real as they can be. Some structural changes are reversible as the postural crossing of the legs as I adjust my posture in the chair. And some, not so much: as you alter the pigmentation of your skin with the tat of your girl-friend's name on your shoulder.

The body documents what the mind does and the fact of this physiological signature is not a disease but a reality of our corporeal psycho-somatic organization.

But let us get back to the point of this blog (and, by the way, if you want a more definitive de-construction of the Disease Model, read Stanton Peele's "Diseasing of America" and Jeffrey Schaler's "Addiction is a Choice;" while at it, you might also check out Santoro's "Kill the Craving" exposure-response prevention protocol).

So, the "steps." I am not opposed to them. In fact, I clinically treasure the vast networking and support resources the 12 Step paradigm has on tap for the folks embarking on recovery. But three of these steps, in my opinion, could stand a bit of revision.

With the above considerations in mind, the 1st, 2nd, and 11th Steps of the 12 Step approach could be reformulated as follows:

Step 1: *"We admitted that while our minds become unmanageable when we are intoxicated, and while we are powerless over having an occasional conditioned craving for drugs and/or alcohol, we do have the power to control our cravings and thus to prevent drinking/using episodes in the future."*

It is, of course, true that once intoxicated, a person's capacity to render effective, strategically-savvy decisions is debilitated to the extent proportionate to the degree and type of intoxication as well as to the degree of one's metabolic processes and tolerance. Consequently, a person is powerless over drugs and/or alcohol when he or she, in fact, ceases to exist as an intact psycho-physiological entity that he or she is at a non-intoxicated baseline. That, however, does not mean that once the person sobers up he or she is powerless to prevent future substance use. The extent of your intoxication yesterday has nothing to do with whether you will or not control your craving to use again tomorrow.

Sure, it's harder to control your cravings when you are "jonesing" than when you are not: but harder doesn't mean impossible...

Step 2: *"We came to know that we, ourselves, could restore us to our functional baseline"*

Note that in paraphrasing step 2, I have replaced the phrase "re-stores to sanity" with "restore to functional baseline." The term "sanity" implies that substance use is madness and therefore retrospectively invalidates substance use as a legitimate, albeit imperfect, form of coping. After all, in order to change, clients need a belief in their sanity; any implication of prior insanity only contributes to unnecessary sense of hopelessness. After all, if past predicts the future, then past insanity predicts future insanity. Clients should not be robbed of their phenomenology as being rational.

Step 11: *"Sought through mindfulness meditation (or other craving control) to improve our conscious contact with ourselves and to control our cravings"*

Re-processing of the Powerlessness legacy in such a way may allow the client with strong prior allegiance to the 12 Step philosophy to retain a modified version of the steps. Most of the 12 Steps, in my opinion, definitely take a person in recovery in the right direction. But, as the evidence on the use of mindfulness in craving control suggests, perhaps, it's a good idea to take a few mindful steps and then to sit down in Zazen (Buddhist "sitting meditation") once in a while.

So, to all you, steppers: march on! Just don't goose-step past the obvious. You have the power to control your cravings. Craving is but another train of thought: step aside and sit down....

The journey of recovery, a millions steps no less!, perhaps, begins with, first, sitting still - transfixed in meditation...

Understanding the Loss of Abstinence through the Banana Peel Metaphor

This essay was first posted as a blog on www.psychologytoday.com in 2008

Slip and Slip Prevention

Say, you are walking down the street and you see a banana peel. When you see the banana peel and realize its slippery potential, you might walk around it in order to avoid a slip. In this see-but-not-slip scenario, you are preventing a slip (Slip Prevention). If you hadn't been paying attention, you would have stepped on the banana peel and slipped - i.e. lost your balance...

Lapse and Lapse Prevention

Say, you are walking down the street and you are not paying attention. So, you step on the banana peel and as a result you slip up - i.e. you lost your balance. Reflexively, you flail your hands and gyrate your torso so as to regain your balance. And voila! - you did not fall even though you slipped. You regained the balance and prevented a fall. In this slip-but-

not-fall scenario you prevented a lapse (i.e. a fall) (which constitutes
Lapse Prevention).

Relapse and Relapse Prevention

Say, you are walking down the street and you are not paying attention.
You step on the banana peel and slip up, i.e. lose your balance. You
flail your hands and gyrate your torso - but to no avail. You are not able
to regain your balance and you fall (i.e. lapse). As you try to get back
up on your feet, you might fall again (re-fall, re-lapse). The three
reasons you might fall again while you are trying to get back up are a)
you got too hurt and it is too painful to get back up, b) you lose your
balance as you try to get up and fall back again, and c) you are feeling a
little shaky and unsteady on your feet and as you have nothing to lean
on or support yourself with you fall back down again. If, however, you
look around, mindfully size up what you need in order to safely get
back on your feet, if, perhaps, you first calm down, maybe rest, and
possibly ask for help to prop you up as you plan to steady yourself once
back on your feet, you just might be able to prevent another fall (relapse) (which would constitute Re-Lapse Prevention).

Review: Slip vs. Lapse vs. Relapse

The Disease Model of substance use does not make a distinction
between a lapse and a relapse. In fact, a slip - a craving, a potentially
transient loss of psycho-physiological balance - is synonymous with a

relapse. Lewis, Dana, and Blevin (1994), in their review of various prevention models, note that the Disease view of addiction "defines the client as either abstinent or relapsed" (p. 171). This catastrophized, all-or-nothing view is based on the idea that "because it is so difficult to fight against the powerful and uncontrollable forces of the disease, the relapse is seen as a probable event" (Lewis et al, 1994, p. 171). What a truly disempowering and dehumanizing prognosis this is, I have to say.

Abraham Twerski (the founder of the Gateway Rehabilitation Center) provides a vignette that has the beginning of the Banana Peel metaphor that had the promise of elucidating the distinctions between the slip, lapse, and relapse. Unfortunately, his own experience of not being able to regain a loss of balance that led to a fall (see below) led to a conceptual denial of an important prevention U-turn opportunity to Twerski's clients.

Twerski (1997) writes that one day he had a package at the mail to pick up and since his car battery was dead he decided to walk to the post-office on a winter day. Twerski writes: "I tried to watch for slippery spots on the sidewalk, but, in spite of my caution, I slipped and fell hard" (p. 118). Twerski continues: "I knew that whether I fell because of the deceptive appearance of the sidewalk or my negligence, I was not going to get to the post office unless I got up and walked, pain and all." In the next paragraph, Twerski continues: "In spite of my painful fall, I was two blocks closer to my destination than when I had started," and adds "This is how we can view relapse. Regardless of its pain, relapse is not a regression back to square one" (p. 118). That is indeed so, but let us regress a bit to the middle of the story. Twerski, in this vignette, experienced a slip (loss of balance), which he failed to control and, therefore, fell, i.e. lapsed. He got back on his feet, by restating his goals (he was interested in getting that package from the post-office) and by decatastrophizing ("I was still two blocks closer to my destination than when I had started"). What Twerski did not do is stay down on the ice, nor did he fall again in the process of trying to get back up or after he got back up on yet another slippery spot.

In summary, Twerski did not relapse. There was no "re" to his "lapse." In retelling this story he, however, misses this important distinction as well as the distinction between slip and lapse and relapse, essentially lumping them together. I wonder what conclusions Twerski might have drawn if he had slipped, flailed his hands wildly, stumbled a few feet forward, and caught himself from falling. Maybe Twerski would have drawn a conclusion that it is not just about watching out for the slippery spots, but also about trying to keep oneself from falling even after one slips up on the icy patch.

Slip: review

Metaphorically, a slip is an act of stepping on a banana peel, losing balance temporarily, but regaining balance, and preventing the fall. Clinically, a slip is a moment of having a craving/desire to use but not using. It's a loss of balance without a fall.

Distinguishing a slip from a lapse makes good sense. An act of slipping does not equal an act of falling - the two are psychologically and behaviorally different events which is reflected in the actual semantics of the words involved: a lapse literally means a fall, a slip does not mean a fall, therefore a slip does not equal a lapse.

A slip is a moment of a craving. A craving is a state of frustrated desire: you want something but you can't have it or you are not allowing yourself to have it. As such, a craving is a momentary lapse of balance. Here you were: all was fine and all of a sudden you feel tempted, out of sorts, out of balance. But just because you lost balance, it doesn't mean that you cannot regain it. Just because you lost balance, it doesn't mean that you have to fall. You can regain balance by engaging in craving control - and this will help you prevent a fall, i.e. a lapse (see below).

Lapse: a review

Metaphorically, a lapse means not being able to regain one's balance and falling but getting right back up. Clinically, a lapse means surrendering to the craving/desire to use and using, i.e. having one substance-using episode, but not returning to original (pre-abstinence) level of substance use. In other words, following the one substance-using episode, you re-establish abstinence.

It should be noted that "using once" is an imprecise definition of "lapse" since, depending on the drug of choice, a "lapse" may involve multiple use of the drug in the context of one using episode. Albeit academic, the distinction between using "once" and "one using episode" is real: while a person may be relatively unaffected after one can of beer and therefore is in a position to choose the next drink while having most of his psychological presence, a person who uses heavier drugs such as cocaine or heroin, in essence, ceases to exist as "a consciously deciding party" until the effects of the intoxication have worn off.

Case in point. Say, you were smoking dope every day. You've quit. Now, at a party, somebody's passing around a joint. You toke up. When the party is over and you wake up the next day, you learn from the lessons of what happened and re-commit to not using. And you go on without using as a result. In this case, your smoking weed that one night was only a lapse. You fell but got right back up... If you, however, went back to smoking weed like you used to, on a daily basis, then that toke would have been the beginning of a re-lapse (see below). If, however, your smoking weed that one night remained an isolated using episode, then, that would be just a lapse. Note that my use of "only a lapse" and "just a lapse" is not an attempt to minimize the significance of your lapse but merely an emphasis to more clearly distinguish between a lapse and a re-lapse.

Applying the same idea to, say, binge-eating. Say, you have been "good" and not binge-eating. But yesterday night you really did it. You stuffed yourself as you were vegging in front of the TV. If your goal was to not binge and you binged, then, what happened yesterday constitutes a lapse. If, after binge-eating yesterday, you gave up your overall goal to not binge-eat and, as a result, return to your habitual binge-eating, then you have re-lapsed (see below).

Or, say, you are struggling with the gambling addiction. You used to gamble online every night after work, but you've quit. On a business trip, while passing a casino, you popped in and blew a hundred bucks. That's a lapse. If, however, as a result, you stop working on the problem (stop going to meetings and/or seeing your therapist), and go back to gambling online, then that's a re-lapse (see below).

But just because you fell (used, binged, gambled) once, it doesn't mean that you have to stay fallen. One fall is not two falls - a lapse is not a re-lapse! To lump these two situations together is to miss an opportunity for a prevention "u-turn."

Relapse: a review

Metaphorically, relapse is falling and staying down. So, re-lapse is either an accident of slipping up, losing balance as a result, failing to regain balance, and, thus, falling (lapsing), and then falling back again until you give up on trying to get back up again. Or it's a conscious choice to return the pre-abstinence level of use.

Distinguishing lapse from relapse follows from the semantics of these two words: suffix "re" means "repetition;" consequently, relapse is a repetition of lapse, and to equate lapse and relapse is to ignore a psychologically and behaviorally valid distinction.

"Homework"

If you are working on some kind of recovery from addictive or compulsive behavior and if your goal is abstinence (from whatever behavior you consider to be no longer acceptable to you), in the weeks to come, as you come across the Banana Peels of your temptations, ask yourself:

"In terms of the banana peel metaphor, what is going on here? Have I just lost balance but regained my balance (just slipped)? Or have I fallen and gotten right back up (lapsed)? Or have I fallen and ended up staying on the ground (re-lapsed)?"

By making sense of "where" you are in terms of your recovery slip/lapse/re-lapse status, you stand to better know what you need to prevent - a slip, a lapse or a re-lapse.

About the Author

Pavel G. Somov grew up in Moscow, Russia. After serving in the Soviet Military and completing his undergraduate degree at the Moscow State Pedagogical University, he immigrated to the Unites States where he pursued a career in psychology. He holds a M.S. in Counseling Psychology from the University of Central Arkansas and a Ph.D. in Counseling Psychology from the State University of New York (at Buffalo).

He has trained and worked in a variety of clinical settings, which include: psychiatric hospitals, university counseling center, county jails, community mental health centers, family medical practice, cancer hospital, veterans' hospitals, pain clinics, and private practice.

Dr. Somov offers an eclectic treatment approach that consists of: Cognitive-Behavioral Therapy, Meta-Cognitive Therapy, Acceptance and Commitment Therapy, Dialectic and Behavioral Therapy, Logotherapy, Mindfulness-based Therapy, Brief-Dynamic Therapy, Motivational Interviewing Therapy, and Eye Movement Desensitization and Reprocessing Therapy (EMDR).

At present he is a licensed psychologist in private practice. Prior to private practice, Dr. Somov, from 2001 to 2003, was the director of a correctional drug and alcohol treatment program in a county jail in Pittsburgh, Pennsylvania.

Peer-Reviewed/Professional Publications:

Somov, P. G. (2008). A Psychodrama Group for Substance Use Relapse Prevention Training. The Arts in Psychotherapy, 38, 151-161.

Somov, P.G. (2007). Meaning of Life Group: Group Application of Logotherapy for Substance Use Treatment. Journal for Specialists in Group Work, 32 (4), 316 - 345.

Somov, P.G. (2000). Time Perception as a Measure of Pain Intensity and Pain Type. Journal of Back & Musculoskeletal Rehabilitation, 14(3), 111-121.

Somova, M. J., Somov, P.G., Lawrence, J. L., & Frantz, T. T. (2000). Factors associated with length of stay in a mid-sized, urban hospice. American Journal of Hospice and Palliative Care, 17(2), 99-106.

Pavel Somov is also the author of "Eating the Moment: 141 Mindful Practices to Overcome Overeating One Meal at a Time" (New Harbinger, 2008; www.drsomov.com, www.eatingthemoment.com).

"*Eating the Moment* is a quick, enjoyable read full of creative, clever exercises and insightful, thought-provoking text. Rather than being shamed into deprivation, readers are taught original exercises to help them learn about their palates and manage their appetites. Who knew that weight control could be so fun and empowering?" —DINA CHENEY, AUTHOR OF *TASTING CLUB*

"In *Eating the Moment*, psychologist Pavel Somov gives you the practical tools you need to reap the rewards of eating more mindfully. Read it and discover how to have a relationship with food that is smarter, healthier, more conscious, and enjoyable." —DEBORAH KESTEN, MPH, AUTHOR OF *THE ENLIGHTENED DIET*

"Somov is one of the most creative psychologists around. He is knowledgeable about research-based and effective therapy techniques. He is aware of Eastern philosophies, and Buddhism in particular. And he is a productive therapist who knows how to translate knowledge into personal action for clients. All of these gifts are evident in Somov's book, *Eating the Moment*, which is not only informative, not only good reading, but also tremendously helpful in the most difficult area of behavior change—losing and keeping off weight." —STANTON PEELE, PH.D., JD, AUTHOR OF *SEVEN TOOLS TO BEAT ADDICTION* AND *ADDICTION-PROOF YOUR CHILD*

"*Eating the Moment* is a thoughtful feast for those who want to understand the psychology of eating and how to overcome mindlessness with food. The 141 eating practices are easy-to-grasp appetizers for becoming more aware, overcoming craving, and transforming your experience with food. If you have ever wanted a primer on eating skills that you never learned at home or in school, this book is an excellent place to start.

—DONALD ALTMAN, AUTHOR OF *MEAL BY MEAL* AND *ART OF THE INNER MEAL*

Made in the USA
Lexington, KY
01 December 2018